FROM SCOTLAND

Edited by Lucy Jenkins

First published in Great Britain in 2000 by
YOUNG WRITERS
Remus House,
Coltsfoot Drive,
Woodston,
Peterborough, PE2 9JX
Telephone (01733) 890066

HB ISBN 0 75431 834 6
SB ISBN 0 75431 835 4

FOREWORD

This year, the Young Writers' Future Voices competition proudly presents a showcase of the best poetic talent from over 42,000 up-and-coming writers nationwide.

Successful in continuing our aim of promoting writing and creativity in children, our regional anthologies give a vivid insight into the thoughts, emotions and experiences of today's younger generation, displaying their inventive writing in its originality.

The thought, effort, imagination and hard work put into each poem impressed us all and again the task of editing proved challenging due to the quality of entries received, but was nevertheless enjoyable. We hope you are as pleased as we are with the final selection and that you continue to enjoy *Future Voices From Scotland* for many years to come.

CONTENTS

Kerrie Gemma-Lee Hume	40
Graham MacLagan	40
Thomas Ballantyne	41
Amy Dawson	42
Catherine Williamson	42
Matthew Burrow	43
Gordon Vaughan	43

Kyle Academy

Natalie O'Pray	44
Heather Dearie	45

Largs Academy

Terri Angela Ferguson	46

Lochgilphead High School

Danielle Gibb	46
Sarah McLafferty	47
Ciara Logan	48
David Robertson	49
Katrina Lowe	50

Lomond School

Scott McArthur	50
Tristan Osborne	51
Claire Paterson	52
Alan Clephane	52
Alexander Holliman	53
Lisa Kilday	54
Neil Calder	55
Harry Esson	56
Rebecca Parry	56
Georgina Fraser	57
Katie Baynham	58
Kirsty Redgate	59
Kirsty Robertson	60
Robert Stevenson	60
Heather Craig	61

Andrew Greer 62
Andrew Pender 62
Euan Mitchell 63
Eilidh Millar 64
Sophie Hope 64
Ciara Taylor 65
Michael Linzee-Gordon 66
Jamie Durrani 66
Carly Humphries 67
Bethany Apedaile 68
Hamish Forbes 68

Plockton High School
Katherine A Smith 69
Miya Komori 70
Marika Komori 71

St Michael's Academy
Claire Price 72
Fiona Craig 73
Marianne Hill 74
Megan Boyle 74
Thomas Williams 75
Michael Dainert 76
Paul Marshall 77
Kevin Dolan 77
Linda O'Neill 78

Vale of Leven Academy
Barry MacLachlan 78
Gillian Parfery 79
Carrie Ann Mcleod 80
Lindsay Hamilton 80
Allem Kerr 81

Wallace High School
Lori Dempster 82
Gary Hammond 82

Fiona Christie	83
Caroline Thomson	84
Nikki Jackson	84
Euan Limmack	85
Steven Conroy	85
Naomi Rimmer	86
Jamie Wardrop	86
Jaqualyn Fisher	87
Rory Mackenzie	88
Murray Wilson	88
Steven Dunn	89
Sidra Hussain	89
Lloyd Davis	90
Jamie-Lee Forson	90
Sara Reid	91
Dominic Willing	92
Barry Maclean	92
Clare Harris	93
James Stewart	94
John Morton	94
Erin McGowan	95
David Sherman	96
Graeme Baillie	97
David Stuart	98
Emily Hutton	98
Gary Miller	99
Katrina Button	100
Andrew Glass	100
Adele Mullarkey	101
Jill Jackson	102
Jamie Aldridge	102
Arron John Russon	103
Liam Dickson	104
Lorna Stewart	104
Anna Murphy	105
Alison Buchanan	105
Billy Honeyman	106
Robert Eadie	106

COLLEGE LIFE

I have started the grand college,
it is exciting, I have to say,
but wasn't really on my first day,
oh so nervous was I,
too scared to even say 'Hi.'

By lunch time it was fine,
I didn't even notice the time,
by chittering and chattering,
muttering and nattering.
Yes, by this time I had made a few friends,
who like me at first were also nervous
and tense.

College is completely different from school,
particularly the mighty rules.
No need to say 'Sir,'
no need to say 'Miss.'
Oh how easy is this?

I am hoping for a degree,
well this is for me.
I might feel a bit queasy
because the work won't be easy,
but surely I will try
and if I don't succeed, I'm sure I won't cry.

Failing this, I must admit,
I'll try again and surely won't quit.

To the best of my knowledge,
I hope to graduate from this college.
I will definitely hold this college memory,
especially on the day of my graduation
ceremony!

Sadia Akhtar (17)

The Glen Of Weeping

Soldiers dying
People screaming
We'll never forget the weeping glen
Houses burning
Smoky air
We'll never forget the weeping glen
Scottish didn't know
English planned it though
We'll never forget the weeping glen
Wives screaming
Children hiding
We'll never forget the weeping glen
Gun shots go
Soldiers die
We'll never forget the weeping glen.

Kirsty Coull

Never Forsake

I left it all behind I thought,
But it has returned.
I must divulge this feeling
Or be confused.
The feeling of love I had for one
Is revealed to my heart.
The faith I have is kept within,
That we're together mentally, not physically.
I've always had the love,
But kept it hidden deep down.
Now it has surfaced again
And is here to stay.
This feeling of love I have for one
I will never forsake again.

Megan McKeracher (15)

The Poems

MISS SNUGGETBUM

Miss Snuggetbum our horrid teacher,
Snorting beast, growling creature,
The other day I talked during art,
She told me off and said 'Right, see if you're smart,
You think that you can talk,'
On went the sum on the board in chalk,
I got it wrong that very sum
And she yelled out 'Are you dumb?'

That taught me to keep my mouth shut,
She said next time my tongue would be cut,
The very next day a boy talked called Billy Stoat,
She yelled the words right out her throat,
'Why don't you go to the headmaster's room
And hear his voice bang and boom?'
When he came back his face was blue,
'Does that learn a lesson for little old you?'

Now we know she likes to shout and ball,
It drives my nerves up the wall,
She's the worst teacher we've ever had,
Not sane, a psycho, she's really mad,
She screams, she shouts, the horrid woman,
She blew the daffodils down, no flowers bloomin'
But thank God the end is here,
We've just been told we've got her next year!

Greig Steven (11)
Annick Primary School

THE RAINFOREST

In the rainforest down on the ground
Lots of trees come crashing down,
Howler monkeys crying for help
But nobody listens to them at all.
Lots of birds in the sky,
Have to move on before they die

But mankind does not seem to care
About habitats of all animals,
Such as bats and wild cats
But lots of people don't have a clue,
Of the damage they can do.

In the morning when animals sleep,
They are woken by a noise like 'Beep beep'
And that means the humans are here once again
With a chain saw that makes a horrible noise.

In the afternoon the animals know
That their home will soon be cut down,
But they are not scared, they are very prepared
But soon they know this hell will end
And nothing will help to mend their home,
And they will be standing there all alone.

Kevin Aitken (10)
Annick Primary School

BLOOD SPORT

Lives cut short
By colours on a shirt,
Where is the sense?
Why must the old war
Be fought by the young?
A sport should not be a question
Of religion,
Yet prejudices from the past
Are still spilling blood,
In the dawn of the new millennium!
It's time now to lay this
Old hatred to rest
And to open our eyes and see
The human being
Through the team colours.

Dionne Doherty (13)
Castlehead High School

MY WORLDS

When I was very young my world was an adventure,
climbing the stairs was like tackling Everest
in my own special way.
When I started school my world was full of dreams.
Fairies, princesses and living in a castle perched on a cloud.
Later, when I was growing up, my world was exciting.
Going so high on swings, my tummy turned upside down
and running barefoot in the sun.
Now that I'm older, my life is changing, things to worry about,
decisions to make like what subjects to pick for years to come.
Life feels different from when I was younger
but there is more to come and the world is my oyster . . .

Lauren McNiven (12)
Castlehead High School

TEACHER CREATURE

I walk into the classroom
Invading its space, I sit quietly
Then, out of nowhere, bang it hits me
A teacher's question
The way he says it is like a laser beam to the head
The pain is the actual question
If you make a mistake - say goodbye
He will look you in the eye
If he catches you you're gone
He can make you delirious
With just one glare
Somehow he can rally your classmates against you
I suspect telepathy
He will not catch me
Then, after a day at school
I thank God that I was not caught.

Ashby Wang (12)
Castlehead High School

MY SUNSET

I sat there transfixed on the beauty,
The sunset like a touch of fire in the fading night,
Out there at the ends of the Earth,
In the silvery shining sea.

A dying phoenix in its watery nest,
The clear horizon; the silence,
Like I was the only person in the world,
The peace and the harmony.

The sun fell and I saw a pale evening purple sky,
I could hear a steady rush of low waves; 'Shh, shh,'
I looked at the water sparkling,
It shone as if refusing to let the sun creep away,
Slowly, silently, slipping . . .
A ghost in the night.

Carefully, cautiously, crawling,
Lingering, reluctant to fade,
One by one the stars began to pop out and sparkle,
My sunset so much splendour,
I love the beautiful sunset on the horizon!

Jayne Ferguson (12)
Castlehead High School

MY WINTER FRIEND

I look outside to where it stands,
a creature that's not properly known to man,
with its body like a shining star.
Glistening in the snow, with a carrot nose
and a smile of stones and arms made of twigs.
A scarf that is wrapped around its football head,
its rugby ball body which is waiting to be blown off
by a whistling wind.
Before I turn off my bedroom light at night
I say goodbye to my winter friend.
In the morning he will no longer stand,
because he will have disappeared
into his winter wonderland.

Lauren Young (12)
Castlehead High School

BLACK AND WHITE

The colour floods in through the window,
But is this place as nice as it seems?
Although so bright and warm,
This world is cold as *ice!*
The lightning strikes,
This is natural pain,
But the explosive boom of the nuclear bomb,
The screams of the soldiers,
This is manmade terror.
We take for granted breakfast, lunch and tea,
But so often forget the less fortunate people,
The refugee with no food,
The homeless, bored drunk drinking to get away from it all,
That could be us one day.
The sick sense of *death!*
Brings fear into my heart,
But I forgive them.
Now I am alone like the last apple on the tree.
For being different I am cursed in the street.
I know not of this place like a baby with no knowledge.
Things we don't know we fear,
We are unique but strange,
We show our fear by bloodshed, killing each other,
We should be here in harmony . . .
Is this *Earth* as beautiful as some say?

Alan McManus (12)
Castlehead High School

THE BEACH

I love going to the beach!
The sand is like silk against my feet.
It manages to get in my hair and in my ears.
You feel like a piece of bacon sizzling away
in the scorching sun.

When the sea water gets in my eyes
they feel as if they are on fire.
When the waves are sky-high they manage
to sweep you back to the shore.
The jet skis go whizzing past and splash
water all over you.

Lots of little children build sandcastles,
some are as big as Buckingham Palace
and some are as small as Kensington Palace.
Some have little moats around them
and others have flags.
Whatever size, shape or colour,
I think they look great!

At the end of the day you are as red
as Santa Claus,
Your hair is full of tangles and is
covered in sand and salt.
I love the beach!

Donna Wilson (13)
Castlehead High School

FIRE

Fire is *evil!*
Fire is a boxer reaching out to hit you.
Fire like an enemy to the human race.
The whoosh of the overdraft scares the firemen.
Fierce fire ripped through the house.
Fire is like a nuclear deterrent ready to strike.

The fire crackles, it sounds like the snapping of a bone,
sound of ice breaking or popcorn popping.
It dances around, jumping like a dancer on stage.
Fire is a bit of the sun which has fallen to Earth.
The flames are orange like the leaves in autumn -
red like an apple, yellow like the wavy corn in a field.

The firemen beaver away but to no avail.
It's like David and Goliath; but Goliath wins this time.
The fire takes another prisoner - the forest.
The charred trees are monuments standing in remembrance
of what once sprawled for miles, whose leaves flickered
in the wind.
But not anymore - it's gone!

The fire burns out.
It is dead,
but so are its victims.

Craig Ferguson (12)
Castlehead High School

MY DOLPHIN

I adopted a dolphin, his name is Whiskey,
He's still very young and very, very frisky.
He lives in Scotland in a very big sea,
The dolphin society look after him for me.

He lives with his family and all his friends too,
He's not caged in, not like in a zoo.
He's able to play with his best friend Splish,
They jump and dive to get some fish.

My dolphin swims in the sea - splish, splash,
He steals all the fish - mash, mash.
My dolphin mates belly to belly,
He has a layer of blubber like jelly.

I've seen him in photos and on video too,
I know he is happy and never blue.
There are people who look after them there,
Just like me they really care.

I hope to go and visit one day,
From where I live, it's a very long way.
If I save up I'll be able to pay
And have the best holiday.

Lisa McCorkindale (13)
Castlehead High School

MY MUM SAYS

'Who do you think you are talking to?'
The words hit me like stones
My 37 year old mum
How?
'Who do you think you are?'
More screaming words
'Your daughter that's nearly 13, remember?'
'Of course I remember . . . stop being so cheeky!'
Mum said growling
I stomped up the stairs, put on my shoes and jacket then . . .
'Where do you think you are going?'
'Out!'
'No you're not!'
'Oh yes I am!'
'Whilst you live under my roof, you will do as I say!'
'OK then I'm going to cause havoc.'
'What did you say?'
'Oh nothing, cheerio, back at usual time,'
Then I slipped out of the door as quietly as a mouse.

Nicola Rafferty (12)
Castlehead High School

SNOW

Snow falls down slow like petals falling from a rose,
It brushes against your skin softly
like when you put your woolly scarf
round your neck so you can keep warm.

In winter it snows because it is the season,
the season for cold soft snow;
like summer is the season we associate
with the scorching sun.

Snow can last forever in the imagination,
but how long can it last?
It can last 'til the harsh beating sun decides
it is time to reappear.

Then you don't see the cold blue mornings again,
at least until next winter,
that's when you'll see again the crisp cold,
slow snow.

Amanda McMenemy (12)
Castlehead High School

RAINBOW

When I see a rainbow, the colours remind me of all
the beautiful things in the world.

Red and orange is the sunset at dusk as it
changes from shade to shade.
Yellow is the warm sun's rays beaming down on me.
Green is the grass, lush and moist with the morning dew.
Blue is the sea at the beach, the white foamy waves
beating off the sandy shore.
It is calm, a huge blanket of blue ocean, covering the Earth.
Indigo is the sky at night with sparkling diamond stars
above like a giant velvet curtain richly covering the sky.
Violet as petals of flowers in the garden,
pearly as an inner oyster shell.
When all these colours and all these pictures are gathered
in a rainbow, I feel as if I'm walking in a world of colour,
my images captured in a raindrop.
As I lie in the grass, surrounded by petals
I watch the sun go down.
The warm rays are beaming down reflecting on the sea.

Eilidh Cameron Nicol (13)
Castlehead High School

AUTUMN

Autumn is the most beautiful season
With the colourful leaves
Gold leaves as crisp as freshly mined gold
Velvet leaves remind me of an orange dress
Which I had when I was a little girl.

Helicopters dance with the wind
Round and round they go until the wind dies down;
Then it is time for their beds.

Conkers fall and roll around the ground,
Children pick them up and see how many they can win
From friends.

Autumn is also a time for Blackpool Illuminations
Bright lights light up your path
They help you see your way in the dark
They are as bright as light can get.

The sun has set and the gold moon shines on the silvery seashore
Dark nights are like death creeping to a desolate island
The dark night is closing in
Winter is here . . .

Kirsty Swan (13)
Castlehead High School

WHY ME?

Why me?
What have I done to deserve this?
Why all the names?
The cheeky comments?
The sniggering,
The jokes,
Why me?

The names hitting me like bricks,
The jokes laughing in my face,
The sniggering as cold as ice,
Black ice,
Why me?
What have I done to deserve this?
I don't understand.

Lisa Scally (13)
Castlehead High School

THE JUNGLE KITTEN

The little marmalade kitten sees the small room
as a jungle, so big and spacious.
She jumps from a chair as if she is a tiger
leaping from a magnificent rock.
She chases a piece of string like a tiger
on a high speed chase after its pray.
She pounces on a cushion like a tiger on its next meal.
She is digging in her razor-like claws and blade-like teeth
like she is a tiger making a kill.
She strides along with her head held high
like a proud tiger on its own land.
But when it is time to settle down,
the marmalade kitten is laying near me
like the cutest little tiger cub dreaming
of being a tiger in the jungle -
leaping, chasing, pouncing and killing.

Lindsay Steele (13)
Castlehead High School

SUNSET

The sun dies for another night
Gradually slipping in its highlight of colours
Slowly falling into a silver sea of stars
And the moon among them
As dawn approaches the constellations
Watch as their forms fade
The sun's rays glow brightly
Once more dusk sets in
And the sun's glowing warmth
Suddenly starts to drop from the sky
And the night air grows cold
And as quickly as night fell down
Appears with the rising sun
Which brings warmth that fills the new day.

Elissa McShee (13)
Castlehead High School

THE TIGER'S RACE

The dark shadow moves slowly and carefully
As it trespasses into foreign land
Watching and waiting in silence;
Looking for a kill
The smell of fear floods the forest.

The eyes of the attacker pierce through the night
And the prey comes into sight
The sky above is dark
Its glittering stars glow brightly
Thrown up just moments before.

Arch enemies are the attacker and prey
At one glance their eyes meet
The race is up!
For both attacker and prey it's between life and death.

Fast and furious they both run
One stumble could mean death
But both hold on with all their might
Swiftly the attacker catches up!
The prey goes down and the tiger wins
Life is calm in the forest
Till next time . . .

Sarah Brown (13)
Castlehead High School

THE CHANGING SEASONS

Summer is my favourite time of year
It reminds me of suntan lotion, beaches and the scorching sun.
The cool air whooshes across my face
Children are having water fights.
Then autumn starts to set in
Leaves fall off the trees like rain falling from the sky
Everything is bare . . .
And cold.
Winter will be coming soon
Snow will fall and ice will be as slippery as a fish
Santa Claus will come down the chimney with his sacks of presents.
Spring will bring baby lambs
The seasons have changed.

Lauren Ramsay (13)
Castlehead High School

DOGS

My favourite pets are dogs
Some dogs are greedy and others are playful
Some are unfriendly and growl a lot
Some dogs are giants compared to others
And others are long or short
You can get spotted or tricoloured looking dogs
With patches on their ears
Fierce and frightening looking dogs or sad looking dogs
Some dogs have small tails and others have
Longer, curly, wagging tails
All dogs are different.

Neil Caldwell (13)
Castlehead High School

WINTER

The season when everything is grey
When trees turn golden brown
When puddles become like mirrors
When birds fly south
When flaky white snowflakes blanket the earth
And menacing looking creatures with carrots for noses
And buttons for eyes roam people's gardens
When animals like the hedgehog and squirrel hibernate
Winter is also the season when Santa clones are at almost every street
When every child is happy because they know that on
Christmas Eve old St Nick will give them a treat.

Marshall Porter (13)
Castlehead High School

LITTLE BROWN MOUSE

Little brown mouse, so simple and small, lives quietly every day
under the stairs at the end of the hall, all tucked up and hidden away.
His bed is a matchbox filled up with old cloth and his armchair
is carefully done by sewing to a pin cushion scales of a moth
whose wings were gold like the sun.

All day he sleeps but at night he awakes to go scampering off
once more to find food and other things to take but also have fun
and explore.
The places are big but common to him as he wanders around
on his own, past humungous and dangerous objects but he's not
frightened that he's alone.

At the end of his adventure he always comes back satisfied
with a good night's catch.
He sits by the fire and slowly unpacks as he takes out pins,
paper and a match.
Mousy is sleepy and needs his bed or he'll get cold and catch a chill.
For outside is what all little mice dread,
There's snow on the window sill!

The other mice are just asleep in their underground tunnels and holes,
So little brown mouse collapses into a heap to hibernate
Amongst the badgers, squirrels, rabbits and moles.

All the animals sleep through the winter, but when Christmas
comes they awake,
To have dances and to skate on the silvery, frozen lake.

Delicate creature so full of skill is alert and sly but kind,
He is busy running his life as he will,
He won't say a word, but he has lots on his mind,
If you're careful you'll see little brown mouse, so simple and small,
Living quietly every day under the stairs at the end of the hall
All tucked up and hidden away.

Iona Hollis (12)
Castlehead High School

My Football Team

I have a dream of a football team
In shirts of black and white
They win the league and the cup as well
To my absolute delight
The North Banks roar just like a lion
The rest of the league just start crying
They conquer Europe, they beat Milan
Vieri, Ronaldo and all
My team you see is St Mirren
So it's just a dream after all.

Sandy Campbell (13)
Castlehead High School

The Thought Lion

I imagine a dark, lonely jungle
Quiet and calm
Which grows naturally
Without help from man.

There lives a huge, bulky lion
With a golden mane
The king of the jungle
Lives up to his name.

His eyes glow bright like gold
His teeth and jaw
Are nothing compared
To his deadly razor sharp claw.

Heather McKinlay (13)
Clydebank High School

THE THOUGHT CAT

I imagine a cat,
Beside a burning log fire,
His black body like a shadow,
Whiskers long, thin and black,
His eyes staring wearily at me.

His nose twitches as I drift off to sleep,
His eyes closing slowly like a setting sun,
Then open large and dark to see me,
He looks tired and old.

I admire his thin slender body,
Long strong legs,
Paws, small nails sharp as daggers,
Then I glance away thoughts wandering,
Immediately my eyes return to look at him,
But the vision has faded.

Sarah Bessant (13)
Clydebank High School

THE THOUGHT DOG

Meandering along,
Looking for love,
The small dog roamed the streets.

His matted fur,
And lolling ears,
With heavy eyes of green.

Sad and lonely,
Is the pup,
Who wants a home and tender love.

Kirsten Hay (13)
Clydebank High School

CHERRY HAS A HAND

They saw some likely looking houses,
Low windows, off the road.
Just some old folks, they said,
And this poodle.

Make sure all's quiet,
Hand the tools,
Easy to surprise
Those silly, old fashioned fools.

Why, *there's* the dog, `
And wagging its tail!
Well, the clock won't bark
And walls never tell.

Admire the jewellery,
The velvet drapes,
The Georgian silver
And the jagged oil paint.

What, who heard that?
A blinking star?
Only the moon, meanders
Across the plunder

Which, as the second ash tree
Is struck by sunlight,
Is still immaculate,
Nothing removed.

Except for Cherry,
That friendly poodle,
Who strangely lingers at
His new-found trophy,

Of two, fresh, human fingers.

Alexis Ferguson (16)
Clydebank High School

THOUGHT CHEETAH

I imagine the beast,
It's coming, it's coming,
I see no place to hide,
I see no place to run.

The cheetah is watching me now,
Watching, waiting,
It smells my blood,
It tastes my fear.

With its deep, black, perfectly formed spots,
I admire its beauty,
Its ears flicker,
Did it hear my thought?

It's moving now like a thief in the night,
Moving slowly, patiently,
While I await my inevitable doom,
It stops, it moves again.

It emerges from the trees
Like a butterfly from its cocoon,
Its form somehow magnified from its surrounding,
It's still coming, still coming.

It's running now,
So very fast, it is running,
As if gliding on ice,
Its body so beautifully designed, so strong.

It's legs are bent,
Ready to pounce like a bird of prey,
I let out a yell, it lingers,
It disappears,
I wake.

Ainslie Boyle (13)
Clydebank High School

THE LITTLE AUTUMN SQUIRREL

I went for a walk in the park
And saw a skinny wee creature,
I stared at it and stared at it,
And saw it had good feature.
Big soft eyes
And a little brown nose,
A big bushy tail
And little frozen toes.

It jumped into a swirl of
Red and golden leaves
And leaped back out again,
With some brown nuts that he had seized.

Amy Douglas (13)
Cumnock Academy

THE SPIDER

Hairy, horrible, hideous,
Long, lean legs,
Black bead-like body,
Tiny, tiptoeing, tickily.

Scuttles, scrambles, scurries,
Climbs, clings cautiously,
Sticky, string, silky web,
Sensitive, silent, slick.

Hastily, hurries, hides,
Surprises, shocks, startles,
Grips, glides, grasps,
The spider!

Laura Moffat (13)
Dalbeattie High School

A COLD DEATH

Bang!
The last red kite falls to its bloody death,
Spiralling down,
Tumbling down,
Until . . .
Smash!
Why did it deserve such a brutal death?
Man's fault!
Man's ignorance!
Man's thoughtlessness!

The last kite has been eliminated now,
So what does man do
About this bloody mess?
Nothing!

He walks away without looking back,
Down the bloody track,
Treading on broken wings, beaks and heads,
Floundering through the pools of cold, red death.

Sean Connor (14)
Dalbeattie High School

RURAL REICH

Test-tube corn stands rigid
Motionless among swaying thistles
Sunburnt ears spread with a summer zephyr
Mingling, mutating
Unseen, unnoticed
Carot
Sickamores grow with seemingly healthy structures
Bark plagued by parasitic creepers
Conniving, consuming
Killing, cursing   .
Cabbbage
Fears escalate surrounding future food chains
Consumers, concerns . . .
Cancers! Modifying
Altering regardless of authority regulations
Genetics generate genocide.

Elizabeth Copland (16)
Dalbeattie High School

EASTERN EAGLE

In eastern lands exotic,
His amber eye hypnotic,
He soars in sun brazed skies,
Ascending on a thermal,
To Eburnean clouds supernal,
An oriental world beneath he spies.

In majestic composure his gaze descends,
To a world on which technology depends,
A neon-stitched city below he sees,
Who would live in such a bustling world of worry?
A hectic life, continual hurry,
When you could be soaring in tranquillity above the trees.

Colin Mackenzie (13)
Dalbeattie High School

I HAVE A PET

I have a pet,
I have to take it to the vet.
I love it very much,
I wouldn't harm or touch.
My pet's name is Mog,
She is a lovely, hairy dog.
If I don't take care
Of every bone and every hair
And don't keep an eye on she,
My lovely pup could die on me.
What my dog needs
Is one or two feeds
And if I don't give,
Then Mog might not live.
I have to take her out,
She will bark and I will shout.
This story was about Mog,
My lovely brownish, hairy dog.

Jason Campbell (11)
Gleniffer High School

My Best Friends

My best friend's are cool,
There's six of them you see,
We talk with each other all the time,
But they mostly talk to me.
My bestest friend is Heather,
Every time we're with her,
There's always lovely weather.
But sometimes we fall out,
Of that there is no doubt.
My old best friend is Claire,
She has short brown hair.
My best friends names are,
Natalie, Vhair, Jennifer and Claire,
I see them almost every day,
And they are always there.

Rosslyn McCool (12)
Gleniffer High School

My Jelly Belly

I have a jelly belly
That is big and wobbly and round
When I'm very hungry you can hear it rumble about
When I'm at the swimming baths I dive from quite a height
But when I land into the pool the water gets a fright
I often get teased about the way my belly is
But all I say inside myself is 'Don't get in a tizz'
I can't wear half the clothes that I really want to wear
But my gran says 'Oh don't you worry
You're just a cuddly bear.'

Elizabeth Stirrat (11)
Gleniffer High School

MY FRIEND NATALIE

My friend Natalie,
She is 12 years old and has brown hair.
I have known her for seven years,
Natalie and I have been best friends for six years.
She has got brown eyes and is 5ft tall,
Her ears are pierced twice and she wants her nose done
And she is moving.
She is always in a bad mood with her wee sister
And has seen the movie Twister.
She likes Britney Spears
And if boys are near,
She'll be there
And that's my friend Natalie.

Heather McLeod (11)
Gleniffer High School

LOVE POWER

My love for you is
Sweet and tender
Although I can't have you
You'll always be mine

Your eyes take over my spirit
And your power over me will
Always be within my heart

Let me be
And still be as sweet as
Sugar for me.

Leighann Anderson (15)
Gleniffer High School

Autobiography Of A Snob!

I am a dude,
My name is Kat,
I was born in March
And that was that,
My mum's tum was no longer fat,
Out I popped and there I sat.

My mum fed me milk,
Straight from the chest,
At cradling and quietening,
My dad did his best,
I did little but eat, scream, gamble and rest,
Okay, I didn't gamble,
But it gives the story some zest.

I started nursery,
When I was three,
It was exclusive,
They chose *me,*
Of course, you had to pay fees,
That sort of thing doesn't come free.

I was brought up in a higher class,
All of my exams, I aimed to pass,
Of course I made it with flying colours,
I'm not like 'all the others',
I was of the 'upper crust',
I wasn't built to mould and rust,
I had life truly sussed,
I wasn't about to go bust.

Kathleen Bryce (12)
Gleniffer High School

FOOD

I dream of food,
Food is the most glorious thing,
It is the best thing in the world,
Sometimes I get in a mess,
But my tastebuds don't care.

Chocolate makes my mouth water,
Custard makes my mouth hot,
In summer when it's hot,
Ice-cream is the one for me, *mmmm!*
Best of all I like all things sweet.

Fruit and veg *yuk!*
Bananas, sweetcorn that's OK,
Broccoli and all things green, *no way!*
I can hear them say eat them up,
But my tastebuds say *yuk!*

Yes it's dinner time,
Guess what I can smell,
It's my favourite dinner,
Lentil soup, sweet and sour chicken,
Apple pie and cream, *mmmm!*

After dinner it's treat time,
Only if I eat all my dinner,
What could it be,
A chocolate biscuit or a cake?
Yes it's a piece of cake.

Food glorious food,
It fills me up when I am hungry,
It comforts me when I am sad,
Food is great,
Food, glorious food.

Gemma Kelly (11)
Gleniffer High School

THE RELATIVES

Oh no, here they come!
Hunchbacked old ladies with walking sticks,
Hobbling slowly up the path.
Moody, sulky, teenagers, annoyed and insulted,`
They were forced to come to a family party.
Old men with dirty bunnets on, impatient to
get to the whisky, beer and lager.
Wee cousins whining and screaming
as they hit each other.
Young mums moaning about how hard it is to bring
up their children.
Uncles talking about football, showing off their best moves.
All of them fighting and pushing to get through the door.
I'm glad they're not my family!

Fiona Kayes (11)
Gleniffer High School

MY ROOM

I don't have a nice room in fact it's a tip,
There isn't a clear space, not even to sit.
My mum's on the warpath I've to clean up the mess,
I don't think I'm old enough but my mum says yes.
She gave me a bin bag to clear out the lot,
I've found lots of things I had but forgot.
I've stacked all my books and CDs in a rack,
It's taken me all week and I've done in my back.
I've polished and cleaned and folded my clothes,
I've tidied my shoes and put them in rows.
Everything in its place it's looking really neat,
I'm going to have tea and flop down in my seat.

Nicola MacDonald (12)
Gleniffer High School

WHY I LIKE SUMMER

Summer is my favourite time of year.
It always means hot sunny days, long nights,
And being off school!
Every year I look forward to the end of May,
Which is when it all begins.

I love the bright colours.
Especially when the leaves on the trees all turn green.
When the brightly coloured flowers bloom.
And the birds chirp happily until late at night.

My dislikes about summer are the wasps and bees.
They invade our homes and gardens.
Another dislike is hayfever.
Your eyes start to water and you start to sneeze a lot.

These are my thoughts about summer.

Vhari Cook (12)
Gleniffer High School

STAR SHINE

Star shine,
Star bright,
Lead me home this winter's night,
As travellers did in days gone by,
Like a beacon in the sky.
You kept the sailors safe at sea,
All I ask is,
Please, lead me?

Andrew Jack (11)
Gleniffer High School

FAST CARS

Lamborghini, Ferrari,
McLaren and Porsche,
They're the fastest cars ever,
They take off with a roar.
Marks in %,
They get a high score.
They're all so cool,
You may even drool.
But if you want to buy,
The price is outstandingly high.
They're the best of their kind,
That you will find.
That is if you get one.

Alan Cunningham (11)
Gleniffer High School

UNDER THE SEA

Under the sea there is life
Beautiful creatures that swim alive
Some are blue, some are green,
Some are colours never to be seen.

Ones that are large,
Ones that are small,
Often I wish I could swim with them all.

One day my wish may come true,
I will swim in the deep sea blue,
And everything I see, I will tell to you.

Jennifer Hamilton (11)
Gleniffer High School

THE CROCODILE

There was a crocodile called Chris
Who said, 'I've had enough of this
Those humans who think they can use
My skin to make a pair of shoes!'

So he thought up a cunning plan,
And gobbled up a passing man
And with the skin he did not eat
He made some trainers for his feet.

So when his friends saw his shoes,
They went all colours, greens and blues.
All his mates said 'Where did you get those,
They look so snuggly on your toes?'

And so when humans are walking around,
Looking so very humble and proud.
With their crocodile skin shoes,
In his home remember Chris,
Who turned the tables on all of this.

Jennifer Law (12)
Gleniffer High School

IN THE MORNING

In the morning I wake up, always in a guddle,
Off to school, pouring wet, walking through a puddle.
At the shops buy some crisps just to get some change,
At the corner turning left, now school is in range.
Almost there, twenty to, no time to stop and talk,
Must get into 2.18 - teacher, blackboard and chalk.
Quarter to nine at my desk, of that there is no fear,
Just in time to hear it said 'Ross Cochran,' - 'Here!'

Ross Martin Cochran (12)
Gleniffer High School   .

THE HAUNTED HOUSE

Ghosts and poltergeists anywhere,
Upstairs, downstairs, everywhere,
Throwing chairs,
With terrible glares,
When you're sleeping they're awake,
Shaking your bed like an earthquake,
Howling in the night,
Gives the ghosts a fright,
They will be back another night.

Marissa Dickson
Gleniffer High School

PEACE

Peace is quietness,
Calm, soft and silent,
Like a ship on a becalmed sea.

Peace smells like a sweet musk incense stick,
Slowly burning away.
Or like a bomb just sitting there,
Tick-tocking all day,
Just waiting to explode,
Bursting into fear.

Peace is like a slice of bread,
The last one in the loaf.
It didn't seem to last as long,
As we'd wished or hoped.

But peace can't all be good,
Peace is also bad.
It can bottle up your feelings,
And make you raging mad.

Peace sounds like a wide open field,
Calm, happy and free.
But it also sounds like the wind,
A warm, cosy breeze.

Peace is like a snow-white dove,
Flying through an empty sky.
Or maybe like a lonely cloud,
Of sweet candyfloss floating by.

But when Winston Churchill
Said '*Victory,*' he meant peace,
The final end to all his fear.
We need Winston back, say it once again,
'Cause we need some peace and quietness,
And prefer the living than the dead.

Mhairi Spence (14)
Inverness Royal Academy

FOOTBALL MANIA!

Shooting down the pitch with the wind in my face,
With the studs in the turf,
Scoring a goal, a wonderful goal hearing the crowd cheer,
But even boys in the park,
With jumpers as goal posts
Will maybe, just maybe become famous footballers.
Then they will be doing the same as me,
Shooting down the pitch with the wind in their face,
And I'll be happy watching them enjoy it.
Soon I'll be old and retired from the game,
But still I won't give up and help people into it,
And watch another new generation coming up,
Into the big league of football mania!

Adam Ferguson (11)
Inverness Royal Academy

THE FLU

Wake up one morning,
Sniffles in your head.
You just don't want to leave,
The comfort of your bed.
Arms are aching,
Legs are hurting,
And you're feeling rather sick.
Something's running down your nose.
Where are the hankies? Quick! Quick! Quick!
Your throat hurts,
From all the coughing.
Sneezing's hurting your nose.
A week of this,
You'll never manage.
Sleep it off, I suppose.
I've just woken up,
And found out, that,
Now I've got the flu.
I've never felt so bad before . . .
. . . *Atchoo! Atchoo! Atchoo!*

Gillian Treasurer (13)
Inverness Royal Academy

SNOW

Snow is glass, smashed into thousands of pieces.
Snow is a satin dress, with sewn-on sequins.
Snow is white heather, spread across the Highlands.
Snow is coconut, from tropical islands.

Snow is icing sugar, dusted over the floor.
Snow is little white shells, lying by the seashore.
Snow is crushed meringue, sprinkled over soft ice-cream
Snow is a lace cloth, the prettiest ever seen.

Snow is whipped cream, fluffy and light.
Snow is diamonds, shining so bright.
Snow is nice white bread, soft and fresh.
Snow in winter's what I like best!

Sarah Myerscough (13)
Kingussie High School

THE LAND OF BIRDS

In the land of birds, far, far away,
A little quail bird ran away.
To make herself a little home,
And to have a big bath with bubbles and foam.

She found a large tree in the middle of the wood,
And set about to make a home as best she could.
She gathered twigs, fern and watercress,
Then put it down in one big mess.

The lift was broken so she took the stairs,
To the perfect branch to lay her wares.
Then she tried her very best,
To make a really pretty nest.

She settled down and laid some eggs,
Soon she had children Betty, Judy and Gregg.
She mashed up fish into pieces and bits,
To put into mouths of three hungry kids.

In the land of birds, far, far away,
A little quail bird ran away.
To make herself a little home,
And to have a big bath with bubbles and foam.

Sophie Mustarde (12)
Kingussie High School

LAMENT FOR A LOST RING

See ma mammy
see ma pal's ring
she piti ona winisill
an ma mammy pitina pucket

See ma pal
she kend a loste ti
am she skelpt ma heed
she sed am no tellny again
ya betta findit oor al skelp yagain
an she deed an a fell an wacked ma heed

Wen a weeked ap
ma pal sed am sa, sa sorry
an ma mammy sed
a kend wher a pit yer ring
ina closit wit ya stockins
an ma pal sed
am no lenten ya any'hin again!

Kerrie Gemma-Lee Hume (13)
Kingussie High School

THE BONFIRE

The bonfire is lit like the Olympic flame,
It flickers like the torch that lights it.
The Guy on top who has come to shame,
Is all dressed up in a running kit.

The trees around like javelin sticks,
Are waiting to be thrown.
While on the ground, there are six
Shot-put hammers which are really pine cones.

Fireworks are bursting in the sky,
Celebrating bronze, silver and gold.
People cheering with voices high,
While toffee apples are being sold.

Graham MacLagan (14)
Kingussie High School

GLEN AFFRIC

A name on a map,
Small 'B' road.
The odd picnic spot,
Recommended to visit,
Picked up a brochure -
'Site of special interest'.

Black sea of Caledonian pine
Soaring to the horizon,
Mirrored in the dark water
Primeval ancient forest.
One time land of wolf
And lynx and bear.

No words can deliver
Sensations of awe and grandeur.
Such remnants of our
Ancient past packed into
Our air-conditioned gentle,
Guide book lives.

Thomas Ballantyne (14)
Kingussie High School

NORTHERN LIGHTS

Thin, fragile handkerchiefs of silk,
Being held in the moonlit sky
By a thousand angels,
Hundreds of miles
Above our minds.

We can never reach them.
But that doesn't mean
That they aren't there.
They amaze everyone,
Flashing before our eyes.

Surreal imagery,
Mystifying and hypnotising,
Leaving us transfixed by their splendour,
Will we ever be so lucky again?
The Aurora Borealis - mind-bendingly alive.

Amy Dawson (14)
Kingussie High School

FRIENDS

Sometimes life is hard,
and it isn't always fair,
ana sometimes,
friends you thought were true,
suddenly don't care.
When words of hate, anger and fear
knock upon your door.
Just remember I'll be there for you,
a friend forever more.

Catherine Williamson (14)
Kingussie High School

THE TEACHER

The ghostly shadows of the classroom,
Silhouetted eerily against the pale walls.
The tall, witch-like figure of the teacher awaits movement,
Her vicious eyes stare through panes of glass.
The cauldron bubbles into action,
as the children begin to move away,
from the smacking of the cane on a desk,
like the pounce of the witch's cat.
She follows her victims out of the room,
After the bell echoes around the school.

Matthew Burrow (14)
Kingussie High School

SHATTERED DREAMS

Sitting in a room with a handful of friends,
Talking of life, of love, of sex,
Mere novices in this game of existence,
Hoping for acceptance,
The topic of sleep comes up, and the images of the mind,
Many laughs are shared, few feelings considered,
Upon asking what I see in my sleep,
I simply reply,
'I don't have dreams anymore.'

Gordon Vaughan (16)
Kingussie High School

HER WORKING DAY

She rises in the morning
cold sunlight streaks her face.
A gentle yawn of traffic
runs down her cheeks - a race.
Stretching her golf-green arms,
running veins in the chase.
A pulsation of people come
heartbeat quickens the pace.

She looks to her friend, dear Arran
who sends a wave or code.
Washing away fatigue, she
switches to active mode.

Her working hours have started,
the tourists meet and greet.
She leads them to her beach front,
where they laugh and paddle their feet.

The afternoon sun strikes warm
Her face absorbs the heat.
As streams of sweat drip down,
the drip, drips to a beat.

The evening now is nigh
Her visitors leave or stay.
She relaxes on her sofa,
watching ships dock in the bay.

She lays her head down softly
Day glides onto night.
On clouds of grass and granite
she gently dims her light.
She slips into the darkness
the end of the day just right.
She shuts her eyes to dream
And snuggles herself in tight.

Natalie O'Pray (15)
Kyle Academy

DEADLY DISEASE

Of all the thousands of people,
Who lose their lives each year.
Whenever I hear the word 'cancer',
I always shed a tear.

I always think of Lee,
Who battled through it twice,
And of my best friend, Nicole's gran,
Who was really nice.

But the instance that strikes me most,
Is when Ronan lost his mam,
You'd think the doctors could find a cure,
But they don't give a damn.

If I said it didn't scare me,
Then I would be lying,
But they have to find something,
To stop any more people dying.

Heather Dearie (14)
Kyle Academy

TIGER

It has eyes like emeralds
And a tail fine and strong,
With claws sharp as razors
And teeth like unsheathed daggers.
Its coat is thick and glossy.
Its body muscular and strong.
The legends are growing
And the folk tale's coming true.
The tiger is disappearing,
Along with its home. ·
I don't think that's fair.
Do you?

Terri Angela Ferguson (12)
Largs Academy

A GHOST TO LIFE

Do not fear me, I bring no harm.
No one knows where I come from.
I walk on water all day long.
No one knows how far I came,
No one even knows my name.
Sometimes I sing out while I float,
But no one ever hears a note.
I sometimes move from place to place,
So no one ever sees my face.
I cannot touch. I cannot weep.
I cannot taste. I cannot sleep.

I can appear then disappear.
I reappear, I'm coming near.
I'm tired of living in my brain.
I feel no joy, I feel no pain.
I do not live, I just exist.
I need to know the life I've missed.
The only ghost within this town.
The only ghost, both lost and found.
But I'm here if you look around.
I'll reappear when you are near.

Danielle Gibb (15)
Lochgilphead High School

I TOLD YOU SO!

See, see I told you so!
Shut it!
No!
Stop fighting!
Keep out of it!
Right, that's it -
no tea for you tonight!
It was his fault he started the fight
Alright, alright
you can have tea tonight.

What's for tea?
Cauliflower and carrots.
It was me. I started the fight.
OK, no tea for you tonight.
Ha, ha, he, he, ho, ho
See, see I told you so!

Sarah McLafferty (11)
Lochgilphead High School

MY HIGH SCHOOL POEM

I woke up in the morning at 5.45,
I felt a little dead but I knew I was alive.

I looked out my window at the crack of dawn,
And I knew the night was really gone.

I had a slice of toast but I felt like a ghost,
So I drank a cup of tea to make me, me.

I went down to the bus and got on with a lot of fuss,
So I sat as fast as fast can be, only Paul and Tony spoke to me.

As I met my peer supporters,
They showed me to my headquarters,

As I was looking round the school,
I felt a bit of a fool.

I got to my first class, RE I really enjoyed it,
Yippeedee!

Then I got to history,
Everything was a mystery.

At lunch the queue was far too long,
I nearly died half-way on.

When I got to maths,
I had to draw some graphs.

As I was going out the school,
I didn't feel such a fool.

As I was getting on the bus,
The day was really worth the fuss.

Ciara Logan (12)
Lochgilphead High School

THE SCHOOL OFFICE

Wee Eddie from S2
And Mrs Cog with the big shoe.
Wee Eddie went off to see the stage head,
And when he came back,
By goodness, was he red.
Mrs Cog asked what this was about,
Naturally we heard her shout.

Now Eddie wouldn't stand for this,
Stormed to the head in a cloud of mist.
Lucky Eddie, he was backed,
And Mrs Cog, she got the sack.
No longer was he in a hole,
But Mrs Cog was on the dole.

Eddie was feeling a wee bit guilty,
And went to see Mrs Cog.
When he got there,
She gave him a stare.
Eddie started to feel hot,
And Mrs Cog, his hide she sought.
No more wee Eddie thought,
She received what she should have got.

David Robertson (12)
Lochgilphead High School

LONELINESS

As I watch the leaves blow,
And hear the wind whistle.
I see the morning appear,
And the sun rises from the loch.

The sky changes colour,
The trees sway from side to side.
It reminds me of the awakening,
And the loneliness of the sea.

As it drifts in and out of the bay,
It is warm with a freezing chill.
It is fearless during the night,
And calm throughout the day.

The sea is a lonely place,
A loner in its kind.
Nobody to tell its troubles to,
Nobody to hear its exciting news.

As I watched the leaves blow,
And hear the wind whistle.
I have seen the morning appear,
And the loch is alone once again.

Katrina Lowe (18)
Lochgilphead High School

SCHOOL!

Summer has gone
But winter is here
Soon we can make snowmen if snow appears

Summer is gone
And winter is here
Now we are at school for another year

Summer is gone
And winter is here
It will soon be the millennium
Because it is near the end of the year!

Scott McArthur (12)
Lomond School

SHOPPING

Shopping all day,
I'd rather play.
In and out of shops,
buying bits and bobs.

Rushing here and there,
people everywhere.
Spending lots of cash,
at sales, it's a dash.

Too many choices,
but, plenty of noises.
Clothes, shoes and posters,
don't forget the coasters.

I have a sneaky hunch,
it could be time for lunch.
Then off again we go,
the sun is getting low.

Shops are closing soon,
look, here comes the moon.
My feet are sore,
stop - no more!

Tristan Osborne (14)
Lomond School

BROTHER AND SISTER

'It's his fault not mine, how dare you blame me?'
'She did it, look at her face can't you see?'
'Oh children, oh children, oh when do they learn?
Tell mummy, tell mummy, it's not my concern!'

'Mummy, he's at it again.
I'm covered in ink, he's flicking his pen.'
'Oh I'm sick of you both, get out of that door!
Go tell grandma, oh what a bore!'

'Grandma, she's pulling faces just too annoy.'
'Oh of course I'm not, what an immature boy!'
'I don't care, I don't care, who does anyway?
Go and be good or no money today!'

'It's your fault we're grounded,'
'You're just annoyed cos you got pounded'
'Beaten up by you, dream on Sis!'
'You're not worth the effort, I'll give you a miss!'

Claire Paterson (12)
Lomond School

A RAINY DAY

Raindrops falling on a rainy day,
When everyone wants to go out and play,
We sit inside and stare out the window,
Wishing the rain could go away.
Everyone's bored stiff with watching TV,
Everyone wants to have some fun,
Play football, tennis or go for a run,
But we're stuck inside,
On this rainy day,
With nothing to do and nothing to play.

The raindrops rattle on the window,
They splatter all over the ground,
They start to make lots of puddles
And floods build up all around.
Eventually we just go out to play,
Tired of waiting around all day,
We come back in at the end of our play,
Soaking wet from a rainy day.

Alan Clephane (12)
Lomond School

RUGBY

In cold, in wet, in snow and in sleet,
We play rugby with soaking feet.
We ruck, we maul, we scrum, all game,
We run and chase the ball the same.

We play in the heat of the shining sun
and with all this we can still have fun.
With a ball over here and a ball over there,
'Hey, come on ref, that wasn't fair!'

We love to win, we hate to lose,
Unfortunately though we cannot choose.
With all this work and no kind of pay,
Why do we decide to stay?

Perhaps it's this I'd like to say,
The team spirit when we play.
It's the greatest game don't you agree?
An international, my aim is to be.

Rugby!

Alexander Holliman (13)
Lomond School

LONER

As I would sit in my corner,
I could hear the voices of popularity
screaming out at me;
'Loner, loner.'
The words buzzing round my head.
And all I could do was sit with
my hands, burying my face.
Feeling the humiliation and sadness
that I wanted to let out so much,
but I knew I couldn't.

Every day was the same.
I dreaded walking in the front gate
to be stared or laughed at.
But why, I didn't know.
As I would walk through the hall,
I heard comments from behind,
some I could take,
but others I just wanted to fall apart.

I felt as though I had a knife
put through me, every time
I walked in that place
and the more I walked, the deeper it got.
I knew people knew I was hurting,
I also knew there was another way out.

Lisa Kilday (13)
Lomond School

AUTUMN FOREST

The autumn leaves float off the trees
like feathers drifting from birds.
Leaves as brown and orange as flames
land with a crisp rustle onto
the frosty autumn ground.

Gradually nature emerges from the silent atmosphere.
Foxes quietly peek around the fallen branches.
Timid squirrels hop towards the early sunrise.
The mild song of a thrush pierces gentle
holes in the sheet of quietness.

As the sun begins to appear,
there is the sound of footsteps.
The foxes quickly sink back into their den.
The squirrels dart up the nearest tree
where they are camouflaged.

It is an early walker climbing the hill
for the view of the sunrise.
An array of wonderful reds and oranges
fill the cool sky
as the sun emerges from beyond the faraway village.

As the day reaches its end, the sun is now a toffee
melting away from sight.
The last leaves have fallen
and the animals are slowly disappearing
to let the new day arrive.

Neil Calder (12)
Lomond School

YELLOW DOG

Yellow dog,
Lying on the grass,
Wags her tail, chews her stick,
Sniffs the air.

Yellow dog,
Rolling in the dust,
Shakes her head, licks her paws,
Looks at me.

Yellow dog,
Chasing after balls,
Barks at cats, snaps at flies,
Young at heart.

Yellow dog,
Sleeping in the sun,
Dreams her dreams, blinks her eyes,
Growing old.

Harry Esson (12)
Lomond School

MY PILGRIMAGE TO IONA

I step off the ferry, onto the shore,
The sacred land beneath my feet,
Onto an island I have never been before,
A holy place I have longed to meet.

I wander around the ruins of a holy place,
Beds of scented flowers bend to greet me,
Gusts of wind blow on my face,
Great peace descends and I feel quite free.

I visit the Abbey, a beautiful building,
Little candles light up the gloom,
I look at a cross with impressing gilding,
See Christ who died to save us from doom.

My pilgrimage is done, I head back for home,
Happy that I've visited the place of my dreams,
I've left my prayers, I'm no longer alone,
The world can be a better place than it seems.

Rebecca Parry (12)
Lomond School

THE GHOST OF GLENCOE

Many a man has attempted here,
The cold, the snow, the windswept fear.
Up the mountains, passed my place,
The deathly sight of the mountain face.

Brave skiers sweep past my reach,
Again since my end I have screeched.
A little girl of three or four,
Has passed the edge, through death's door.

I remember my own loss of life,
Blindly through a blizzard, my cheeks were sliced.
Over the edge and rendered alone,
My friend, my father, wide-eyed he roamed.

The mountains around me listened well,
To my misfortunes, echoing like a sea shell.
Yet the searchers did not hear my voice,
It was much too silent, maybe by choice.

Georgina Fraser (11)
Lomond School

THE RAINFOREST

Humid air, stuffy atmosphere,
Hot sun beating down
Between cracks,
In the canopy of green;
Tall trees,
Reach to the sky,
Stretch out their arms,
To hold hands with their neighbours,
Solid trunks,
Ridges of bark,
Swathe the skeleton within;
Snakes dissolve into the background,
Merge into the scenery - camouflage, nature's miracle,
Awaiting their innocent prey;
Monkeys chatter busily,
As they go about
Their daily work;
Insects in the thousands,
Roam the carpeted floor,
Spiders, termites, mosquitoes buzzing;
Poisonous frogs,
Yellow, red, green, flashing warnings,
Startling predators;
Woodpeckers indulge in tropical wood,
Parrots swing from the vines;
Vivid hues contrast from brilliant greens,
Pink flamingos drink from the riverbank,
Keeping a watchful eye out just in case;
Suddenly, a drop of water falls,
The monsoon has begun . . .

Katie Baynham (13)
Lomond School

BOOKS

Books may seem just boring,
But when you get into them, they're quite different.
Some are fairy tales, some are horrors,
Some are romances, some are true.
But anyone can read them,
It's not a skill!

Books are like dreams,
They can take you anywhere,
They can take you to Hollywood,
They can take you to the wild west,
Or the mystical east, but remember,
It's not a skill.

Most books are happy,
Most books can be sad,
Just pick your choice
And get stuck in,
But remember to use your imagination,
Don't be upset because
It's not a skill.

Some have happy endings
Some end quite bad
But every book is the same
And that is, they're good.
Once you start reading,
You just can't stop, to put it away!
Nope, because that's
One hard skill.

Kirsty Redgate (13)
Lomond School

THE SHIP OUT AT SEA

The dark, misty night creeps in,
The light from the lighthouse should be within.
I'm sitting here upon the rocks,
Watching the people on their evening walks.
Then suddenly silence comes and a foghorn from a ship is heard.
Everyone was shouting 'She's in trouble, she's in trouble!'
A faint crash was heard and no one could be more silent,
Listening for a signal to say the passengers were safe.
But nothing, nothing but a seagull squealing.
Thoughts were in people's heads whether to phone for help
or would it be too late?
Was there anyone I knew on board that ship?
What if that was me?
Finally someone said something, a man who lives beside me,
Mr Parsons who is stout and wee.
'I'm sure there is nothing much left to see.
Go home and comfort those who need it.'
I didn't go home, no one did; everyone just sat on the rocks
staring out to sea. Thinking thank goodness it was not me.

Kirsty Robertson (13)
Lomond School

A WALK IN THE WOODS

All the trees together form a sort of roof.
The ground is damp and squishy
and littered with leaves.
With every step my boots get
clogged with mud.

Only a few patches of sunlight
make it through the trees to dry up
the brown squishy mud which is
covered with leaves of amazing
colour brown, golden, orange and red.

Then a sudden burst of sunlight
hits my face as I leave the
wood and come into a beaming
sunlight of a beautiful day.

Robert Stevenson (12)
Lomond School

IN THE WOOD

In the wood the trees are so tall,
I feel so very small.
On the floor there are millions of pine needles,
All of the needles have turned brown,
All the ones which have fallen down.
When they're on the trees they're green,
Green like they have always been.

Up above in the tall trees,
There is a gentle breeze.
The trees are swaying,
Swaying and swaying.

I hear the stream flow,
I don't think it's going slow.
The water must be so cold,
Well so I've been told.

The weather is sunny but quite cool,
Not the weather to go in the pool.
The birds are cheeping
And the grasshoppers are creeping.

I feel so relaxed in the wood,
When I'm in the wood I feel so good.

Heather Craig (11)
Lomond School

AUTUMN LEAVES

Rustle go the leaves
Crack go the twigs
On a crisp autumn day
The colours are aglow
Brown, orange and yellow.

Falling, falling through the air
The wind lifts the leaves
Over gardens and fields
They drop on their way
In bundles they stay.

The wind whistles through the trees
Taking the leaves one by one
Soon none will be left
The branches will be bare
Autumn is ending and winter is near.

Andrew Greer (12)
Lomond School

A WINTER WALK

Walking through the winter woods
Snow and leaves crunching beneath my feet
Birds are singing high above
Calling out through the crisp winter air

A fox pokes his head out of his den
To see who is passing outside his home
Snowflakes float down to the ground
As he retreats to the warmth at the back of his lair.

All is white and all is calm,
As I continue to journey through the woods.
In his winter coat and colours
And playing joyfully is a snow-white hare.

Nearing the end of my icy walk
I climb a tree to see what I can see.
In the distance I see my house and know
That I will be returning there, without a care.

Andrew Pender (12)
Lomond School

COLOURFUL WINTER

As the morning sunlight cuts
Through the crisp, sharp air
Illuminating the forest,
Cutting through the dense canopy,
The forest drips with
Emerald dew drops.

The cold animals shrink away
To the warmth of their dens.
The sun melts away
Like butter on hot toast,
Yet still the forest is drenched in green.

My heavy walking boots
Crunch through the glazed mud,
The grass blades shatter and crack.
But even now
In mid-winter,
The forest is still green.

Euan Mitchell (12)
Lomond School

AUTUMN COLOURS

Autumn colours in the trees,
Blowing softly in the breeze,
Birds fly swiftly on,
Before the cold winter comes.

Squirrels gather lots of nuts,
Hiding them carefully in the ground,
Where they can be easily found,
But the squirrels always forget.

Autumn colours on the ground,
Children scatter them everywhere,
They blow away every day,
Until the ground is totally clear.

Eilidh Millar (11)
Lomond School

THE HURRICANE

The hurricane is coming,
Coming over the sea.
I smell danger in the air,
As the wind blows on me.

The hurricane is coming,
From far, far away.
Coming to wreak havoc,
At the place I stay.

The hurricane is coming,
An eerie silence falls.
It's very near now,
I wait until it calls.

Sophie Hope (12)
Lomond School

CHRISTMAS!

Christmas is just great,
I love that time of year,
It's time for family and cake,
It makes me want to cheer!

Christmas is just great,
Especially if it's a white one,
It makes my mood inflate,
But not if I slip on my bum!

Christmas is just great,
I wish it was the big day,
I'm so excited I can't wait,
Unfortunately it's only May!

Christmas is just great,
A good time of year to remember,
I've already got presents for my mates,
But aww, it's only September!

Christmas is just great,
Just one month till it's here,
These mince pies taste out of date!
Oh no! They're from last year!

Christmas is just great,
I'm wishing for loads of snow,
I hope Santa isn't late,
Cos there's just one night to go!

Ciara Taylor (12)
Lomond School

AUTUMN FOREST

I walk through the golden forest,
hearing water trickle off the trees
and into bright silver puddles;
Listening to the wind brush through
holly bushes and squirrels diving
through the leaves.

As I wander further on, leaves crackle
under my feet,
Twigs snap as animals go to hunt.
As I leap over large wet logs,
covered in thick damp green moss
I trip and land in a puddle.

It was fresh and smelt of the forest,
yellow-brown leaves fall off the trees.
The sun is glinting off the droplets of rain
then I realise that I was at the end
and in front, lay the meadow beyond.

Michael Linzee-Gordon (12)
Lomond School

MY RABBIT

My rabbit learned to jump a hoop,
To fly a plane
And loop the loop.

My rabbit can jump to ten foot high,
To reach up far
And touch the sky.

My rabbit learned to swim a lake,
To work an oven
And bake a cake.

My rabbit likes to watch TV,
To read a book,
Or play with me.

My rabbit learned to wrestle a toad,
To catch a fish
And cross a road.

My rabbit managed to break free,
To run away
And escape from me.

Jamie Durrani (13)
Lomond School

THE WOODS

In the spring the new leaves come,
they bloom with lovely blossom.
But soon enough they fall again,
to the ground beneath them.

The summer comes
and children play.
They climb the trees
and feel warm breeze.

The orange leaves trickle and turn,
but when they land they topple.
For people come and nap on them
which doesn't make them happy.

It's cold, it's snowy,
the wind is at its worse.
The rainy nights hammer trees down,
but soon new trees will be planted.

Carly Humphries (12)
Lomond School

FOREST SEASONS

The fresh green leaves of spring
The new coloured flowers that bring
Bumblebees and people who sneeze
Rabbits and birds that sing.

The summer's radiant sun
Lots of children having fun
Inside the forest, animals among us
Until the day is done.

Autumn leaves fall to the ground
There's plenty of nuts and fruit around
Squirrels play, hide nuts away
In larders underground.

The cold, crisp winter air
Animals hidden in their lair
The moon aglow upon the snow
The forest's trees stand leafless, bare.

Bethany Apedaile (12)
Lomond School

WINTER WALK

I walk through the snow,
crunching at my toes,
I look up at the trees,
snow falls on my nose.

I'm all wrapped up,
in my winter gear,
thick jacket and hat,
through my scarf I peer.

The clouds are heavy,
they hang in the air,
the snow storm is over,
the sun must be somewhere.

The sun peeks over the mountain,
it warms up the frosty ground,
the cold snow melts,
into puddles all around.

Hamish Forbes (12)
Lomond School

THE HOLOCAUST

H olocaust
O f the Jews
L iving is not an option
O verwhelming numbers dead
C ause of death, unknown
A ny way of killing, accepted
U nacceptable pain, death
S uffering
T hey are people too, living, breathing, alive.

Katherine A Smith (12)
Plockton High School

THE ROAD I CHOSE
(With apologies to Robert Frost)

Like Robert Frost, I too have stood
Where a road diverged in a yellow wood
And wondered how to start to try
To choose the road I'd travel by.

Both roads that morning modest lay
A quiet hour in a quiet day
And yet the air was fraught with choice:
When I chose my road, would I rejoice?

Or would I have made a grave mistake -
My chosen road would I forsake?
Would I be glad, or would I rue?
I knew not what I ought to do.

I looked again to each road's bend
But neither had a simple end.
I knew not which would lead me well;
Both 'equally lay' I could not tell.

Finally, I made up my mind
And shut my eyes to the road behind
Started down my chosen path
Which somewhere ages and ages hence
I'll find has made all the difference.

Miya Komori (15)
Plockton High School

HE HAS A COLD NATURE, MY CHILD

'He has a cold nature, my child,
He runs his cold, white hands over the land.
He makes everything shiver and cold, my child.
He's never been seen although everybody knows about him.

The plants shrink away in fear as he passes.
Their merry, green faces hide as he comes.
The lakes freeze in terror, my child
And the animals hide in the ground.

He's fast, my child, yet he lingers long.
He makes the fires look merry and bright.
He's never been known to forget to come
And he just lives on and on.

When he runs, he howls like a demon, my child.
The trees shake their bare branches at him.
He clings to the window and tries to hold on,
But only the sun can defeat him.'

'Who is he, oh Mother, who is this devil
Who lives on and makes the trees angry?
Why is he so cold and bleak?'
'My dear, my dear, he is Winter.'

Marika Komori (13)
Plockton High School

A DAY AT CRUACHAN CROFT

A day at Cruachan Croft,
Is a day of fun and pleasure.
Get ready for a fun day out,
There are lots of things to do.

A day at Cruachan Croft,
You have lots of activities to do,
From abseiling to water skiing
And lots of games too.

A day at Cruachan Croft,
There is lots to do and see;
The beautiful sunrise,
The beautiful sunset
And all the hills around us.

A day at Cruachan Croft,
Breakfast in the morning,
Dinner in the evening,
Between those a few wonderful hours
Of fun, games and pleasure.

A day at Cruachan Croft,
Running in the field,
Playing hide and seek,
Jumping up and down.

A day at Cruachan Croft,
Everything is getting dark,
Lying in our beds,
Thinking about tomorrow.

Claire Price (13)
St Michael's Academy

VOLCANO

The big monstrous
triangular shaped mountain
sits proudly upon the hill
with its huge cone shaped nose
pointing into the air.

Steam rises up into the sky
bubbling and spitting
Noises begin to louden
people start to run.
This is it, it's going to erupt.

Deafening bangs, explosive bombs
being fired out of its mouth
Poisoned gas slowly covers the village
Abandoned settlements stand in fear
of the raging burning lava.

The grey ash covers the roads
Orange flowing lava destroys houses
burns the crops
The lava contaminates the water
while the fish burn

Rescue teams are called in
to help save the burning village
People's houses and belongings
being destroyed by the scorching lava
and people cry for help as they discover
their loved ones are lost.

Fiona Craig (13)
St Michael's Academy

MY WEE, GREEN FRIEND

Far in the distant universe,
A million light years past,
A galactic being roosts,
We don't know much about him,
But I knew he was real.

He landed outside the croft,
We greeted each other with a smile,
Together we flew across the galaxy,
He showed me the rings of Uranus
And went for a walk on Mars,
Venus' moons were a wondrous sight
Pluto was so cold and lifeless,
So cold we couldn't land there.

Earth was our next destination,
We entered the Milky Way,
Flew past Ben Nevis,
Forth and Clyde Canal,
We landed back at the croft,
Said our goodbyes,
But no one believed me the next day.

Marianne Hill (13)
St Michael's Academy

STARS AND SPACE

Stars that glitter in the sky
Looking like a little firefly.

Planets, comets, night and day
Dark and light, that's Mother Nature's way.

Hot and cold, that's what divides the year
The planet ending; that is our fear.

Fly to the moon, build houses on Mars
Our minds keep going, thoughts of futuristic cars.

We all love our planet
So let's stop destroying

And start helping
The planet we live on.

Megan Boyle (13)
St Michael's Academy

IN THE PLAYGROUND

Ring! Yes, it's break time,
Time to go out and play,
I take out my sweets,
Then I go and play football,
Twenty seconds flat and my Mars bar is finished,
The school janny, Old Smithers is watching for any bad kids,
Nobody will dare cross his path,
The girls are talking and others are cheering us on,
Primary ones splashing about in the puddles,
The school bully is getting told off by Old Smithers
For tripping a wee girl up,
The people who bring our lunch are here,
Yes! I scored a goal,
My team is winning 3-2,
Ring! Break time is over,
Time to go back inside now
And do my sums,
Well, see you at lunchtime!

Thomas Williams (13)
St Michael's Academy

THE DEER

Under the cold and wetness of the morn
I crept around the dewy grass
Which held the smell of deer
I locked and loaded
And pulled the pad upon my shoulder
When I heard the sound of hooves
Flashing with soft moistened ground
I slid hand on stock and trigger
Place barrel on old dead birch
And wait, pointing barrel at the clearing
Where sunlight sparkles on the wet grass
There she was
The large brown deer looked graceful and calm
Until I shot
Bang!
She hit the ground
As my excitement turned to sadness
I dropped the gun
Walked over
And saw to my dread
She had died
With a shot to the head
I shed a tear.

Michael Dainert (13)
St Michael's Academy

THE SEASIDE

It's a scorching hot summer day
And we're off to the seaside.
My friend and I can't wait to play,
I hope when we get there it's low tide.

My friend and I build sandcastles,
Whilst Mum and Dad splodge on the sun cream.
Mum goes and gets cockles and mussels,
Whilst I lick my ice-cream.

The day is nearly over,
Dad packs up the car
And we depart from Dover,
Thank goodness home isn't that far.

Today has been a wonderful day,
Where everyone could rest and play.

Paul Marshall (12)
St Michael's Academy

WITCHES' BREW

A packet of crinkled crisps
A sachet of cream carrots
A tin of baked beans
A bottle of orangeade
A touch of salt and bring to the boil
    Fizzing and popping
    Bubbling away
    It's very tasty
    I'll have it today
    But leave some for you.

Kevin Dolan (12)
St Michael's Academy

STORMY

Shivering and cold the field mouse cowered in the wheat field,
The thunder crashed,
The lightning bolted and trees were split.
Everywhere the mouse ran something would stop him,
He darted in all directions,
Trying to stay alive was a challenge.

The rain grew heavier and was thrust one way then another by the wind,
The mouse ran to the perimeter of the field,
The lightning bolted one last time,
A tree in the small defenceless mouse's path was split,
It was toppling at a great speed,
The mouse ran as fast as his four scurrying legs would take him.

The tree toppled and missed the mouse,
The rain lightened and the thunder stopped,
The storm was over and the mouse scurried to the safety of his den,
He snuggled down to sleep and thought to himself,
Tomorrow is another day.

Linda O'Neill (13)
St Michael's Academy

HOMELESS

H igh as we stand people look down on us.
O f all the money in the world, I have none.
M um? I have no mum. The gutter is my mum.
E verything I need, I don't get.
L augh? I have not laughed my whole life.
E ven when I beg I get no money.
S pare some change please.
S pare some change . . .

Barry MacLachlan (12)
Vale of Leven Academy

TOUGH WORLD

There's a boy who lives at the bottom of my street
His name is Liam I think
His mother died when he was young
And his father likes to drink.

He has no other relatives
It really is a sin
His clothes are so repulsive
Some say he found them in a bin.

In school he has no other friends
He has to eat lunch on his own
One time I tried to talk to him
But he told me to leave him alone.

He struggles with his schoolwork
He isn't very nice
He's always getting in trouble
And has been suspended twice.

Sometimes I wonder what he has done
To deserve such a terrible life
Does he curse and swear at his granny
Maybe he killed his father's wife.

Whatever he's done it sure is sad
To see him sitting in school
He sits alone, he has no friends
His life is certainly not cool.

Gillian Parfery (11)
Vale of Leven Academy

MY POEM

He would go to school
Come home from school
Ask for dinner
His father says get it yourself
2 shillings to last
Because we live in the past
Your mother ran away
With the postman
Come on, come on now
Time to waste   .
We've got to get to the pub
Before it is too late
His father runs and runs
Faster he goes
Just to get to the pub
Free drinks to go
Strong his heart just can't
Wait till twenty past eight
School is coming faster and faster
Got to got to bed
Dinner's tomorrow.

Carrie Ann Mcleod (12)
Vale of Leven Academy

POVERTY

Whenever I go to school
People laugh and say I'm not cool
I don't want to be cool
I just want to live and go to school

When I go home, I go to my room
It's so small, I feel like I'm in a tomb
I don't want to die and stay in a tomb
I just want to live and go to my room

When my dad comes home
All he does is moan and groan
He tells me this is not my home
And then he just moans and groans.

When I go down for my dinner
My dad always says I'm not a winner
I don't want to be a winner
I just want to go downstairs and eat my dinner.

Lindsay Hamilton (12)
Vale of Leven Academy

DIFFERENCES

'I'm rich and have plenty of money.'
'I'm poor and have nothing.'
'I get a lift to school in my dad's estate.'
'I walk to school, hot or cold.'
'I get £10 pocket money every week.'
'My family gets £10 a week.'
'I have millions and millions of dolls, each different.'
'I have one doll, broken and dirty.'
'I live in a huge house, three stories high!'
'I live in a small house, with two bedrooms.'
'I have my own room, coloured pink.'
'I share a room with my two brothers, it's white.'
'I get huge dinners, whatever I want.'
'I get one slice of bread and butter each night.'
'Yes, I'm rich all right.'
'OK, I'm poor but does that make me stupid?'

Allem Kerr (12)
Vale of Leven Academy

CAGED ALIEN

As I glared out the cage
My green slimy but warm fingers pressed against the bars
It came with a box of food
I started jumping about, it filled my bowl
I smelt the air, mmm, it was ground up soil and grass
It went away, I started to eat

Soon it came back with something
Something round and yellow
I ran and it moved
Like some sort of boulder rolling
I tried to get out but couldn't
I was trapped in some sort of cage
Like I had done something wrong
As if I was a *prisoner.*

Lori Dempster (13)
Wallace High School

IT'S TOO LATE

I look around and I see space
I look around and there are huge buildings all over the place
Space, the final frontier
Space, everyone's been there
I look up in the sky and birds fly by
I look up and there is not a bird in the sky
The sun shines and gives out light
The black clouds cover it and it always seems like night
Please don't destroy this totally amazing place
It's too late this totally amazing place has gone.

Gary Hammond (13)
Wallace High School

IF THE MOON . . .

If the moon was made of cheese,
We would never ever go hungry,
Except maybe in a thousand years,
When it would be all green and mouldy.

If the moon was close enough to reach,
We could pull it down out of the sky.
Maybe it has a magical power,
Maybe it can make us fly.

If the moon had magical powers,
What would they be?
You can use your imagination,
But don't ask me.

If the moon had hands and feet,
It could jump around the sky.
It could come down to us on Earth,
Or maybe it's too shy.

If the moon was an alien,
Just what would it be like?
Would it have twenty legs
And could it ride a bike?

If the moon had wings,
It could fly like a bird,
It could fly through the air,
Without being heard.

Fiona Christie (12)
Wallace High School

MRS MILLENNIUM

The millennium approaches,
Then you will hear,
People wishing each other a happy New Year.
Bells will be ringing,
Glasses will be clinking,
Because she has arrived.
She comes all dressed up,
You can see the party mood in her eyes.
Children upstairs asleep in their beds,
Adults down below celebrating until the sky goes red.
The sun comes up, the moon goes down,
At last the millennium is here,
But she will not come again for another 1000 years.

Caroline Thomson (13)
Wallace High School

MARS IS MADE OF . . .

Mars is made of Mars bars
The moon is made of cheese
The Earth is made of green and blue
A bit like you and me

The Milky Way is obvious
So is the galaxy
But Venus is a puzzle
Just like Mercury

That's what people tell me
But one day I'll go and see
I'll float up to the sky
And eat the whole galaxy.

Nikki Jackson (12)
Wallace High School

WORKING LIFE

I have a robot,
His name is 607 Rot.
All he asks for is oil but he needs a lot,
It keeps him running on things he's got.

He does most of the dirty work round the house,
He can make a 10 course meal but he can't catch a mouse.
He shuts himself down at 8 o'clock,
He can't move a joint, he's as solid as a rock.

Sometimes I feel sorry for my robot friend,
He'll work all his life until he comes to his end.
Does he have feelings like us or maybe more?
Could he ask another question like you'll see in verse 4?

I got him about two years ago,
The rain had stopped, it started to snow.
I'll never forget the first thing he said,
'What's all this powder pouring on my head?'

Euan Limmack (13)
Wallace High School

SPACE

I would fly you round the universe in a three wheeler car,
I would take you to Jupiter,
Would there be aliens or Martians?
Would they be green or yellow or would they be multicoloured?

What shape would they be?
Would they have human features?
Or would they look like humans?
Who knows?

Steven Conroy (12)
Wallace High School

THE RIDDLE FOR ALL TIME

What spins round a clock,
But is not a hand?
What stretches for miles,
But is not a land?
What do you always plan,
But is not a task?
What is always near,
But just out of grasp?
What flies through the air,
But is not a bird?
What screams to be heard,
But won't say a word?
What do we never reach,
But always want to know?
What answer hides here,
But not from its foe?
What's weird and unknown,
But no centaur?
The answer you seek,
Lies in the *future*.

Naomi Rimmer (12)
Wallace High School

FUTURE CITY

This is my city that I despise,
The neon-tipped buildings look down like eyes.
They loom like trees blocking out the light,
In the depths of the city it is always night.

Like a swarm of ants surge through the maze,
Their faces long and in a daze.
Crazed bikers cruise the dangerous city,
And for the poor and homeless, there is no pity.

If you're lucky you can run to Mars,
There, peace and tranquillity rule by far.
Everyone hopes to escape this crowded place,
This is the wish of the human race.

I fear what the future holds,
Only time itself can this be told.
This is the nightmare of my world.

Jamie Wardrop (13)
Wallace High School

THE MILLENNIUM DOME

I stare dead-eyed out the window,
Scanning the buildings for anything to gaze at.
All I see is still, industrial grey,
Then in my peripheral sight,
My eyes come upon a monument.
A huge, displeasing dome structure,
I hate it,
Teachers make us go on school trips,
Parents think it's good to learn about the past, *booorring,*
I loathe it,
All that money wasted on an annoying monument,
People thought it would give back what it took.
Boy were they *wrong!*
Those millions of pounds wasted on a Dome,
Money for the homeless,
Money for pensions,
Money for housing,
Money for *us!*
It gets me really worked up every time I look out that stupid window.

Jaqualyn Fisher (12)
Wallace High School

FUTURE THOUGHTS

Gazing into the future, the crowds of people see,
their dreams and their fears, in front of you and me.

Could there be a flying car, or a virtual reality set,
but will there be the growth of the dreaded cigarette.

Just imagine robots, jerking through our dirty work,
but there is the dreaded devil, climbing to Earth with his fork.

With crime at a low, and rubbish non-existent,
but are there bloodthirsty aliens, thriving on a mission?

No more dreadful tornadoes, or extreme hurricane winds,
but will there be more criminals not feeling guilty for their sins?

I feel scared about what will happen to all our hopes and fears,
I hope that all my dreams come true, in the next fifty years.

Rory Mackenzie (13)
Wallace High School

PLANET POEM

The sun, the massive blazing star.
The moon, the dull planet from afar.
Pluto it's much colder than the star,
It is many miles, way too far.
The rings of Saturn, ice cold dust.
Earth blues and greens the planet
That is now not so clean.

Murray Wilson (13)
Wallace High School

THE GENETIC MONSTER

Genetics it's so, so bad,
It likes to get rid of your mum and dad.
It makes things different from the others,
Or a clone the exact same as their mothers.

We don't want birds with three legs,
Or flying monkeys which have two heads.
We don't like another of what we had,
It makes the first one look so sad.

These scientists should be put away,
So these new animals aren't here to stay.
We better stop this genetics game,
Before everyone has the same name.

Steven Dunn (12)
Wallace High School

THE MILLENNIUM IS HERE

I love the fact the millennium is here,
Another occasion to celebrate a new year.
Goblets are clinking I hear in my ear,
Children of the new millennium are cannier,
Than the children of the last who were briskier.
I beckoned the millennium to come near,
I said 'Behave well, I make it clear,'
There is still something I think I fear,
Today will I get some beer?
The millennium gave me a slight peer,
I shivered all over full of fear.
Then he came right up to my rear,
And asked me politely 'Would you like some beer?'

Sidra Hussain (12)
Wallace High School

2050 V 2000

Today the Earth is an old blown-out fireplace,
It just couldn't keep up with mankind's pace.
I blame the older generations,
Too busy with their money-making creations.
And in 2000 when they had the time they needed,
Most of the problems they should have faced, were not heeded.

Yes, well you would have done exactly the same,
Could you give up all that you had when you were ahead of the game?
It was certain to happen from 100 years before, it was fate,
We didn't mean to leave you the Earth in such a terrible state.

It's never too late to solve a problem when you have real
determination and a plan,
And I reckon I could do something,
Even though I'm just one man.

Lloyd Davis (13)
Wallace High School

GLOOMY EARTH

In the year of '99,
Oh what a hygienic and unforgettable time.
But here we are in 3003,
There's nothing here you would like to see.

The cities are dark and outstandingly dull,
Most of the people here are fatally ill.
The chimney pot smoke is exceedingly black,
The thought of the world is dark, dark, dark.

We have dreaded this for years,
But now it's too late, we've bottled our fears.
We were laid back when we should have taken action
As for our world, there's not a nice fraction.

So people out there this is not a joke,
We can't go on living in this thick black smoke.
The land could be bright and exciting,
Instead of being foggy and frightening.

Jamie-Lee Forson (13)
Wallace High School

THE PRICE IS NOT RIGHT

Will the skies get darker
Or will the people stop
Polluting the world without any thought?
Will the forest have disappeared
The thing we all have feared?
If we go forward we can't go back
To change the things that are black.
Everything we do in every way
We are destroying the world day by day.
We think this is a dream
That's the way it all may seem.
But this is truly real life
Who's destroying the world you, your life.
Simple things like deodorant and hairspray
They destroy the world in a different way.
We all have a right to the world
So we shall fight for what we know is right.
If the future is gloomy and dull
It is only you who has to pay the bill.

Sara Reid (13)
Wallace High School

3038

In the year 3038 the Earth might be forgot,
You might be happy on the moon or you might not.

We could meet other creatures, hairy, big and small,
Whatever is out there it won't be like our big blue ball.

You won't have any freedom to run and jump and play,
It will be very different but you'll be there to stay.

Every hour of every year it always will be light,
You won't see the moon shine, it won't be truly night.

The landscape will be different, no plants, no trees, no green,
So before you move way up there, think of what has been.

Dominic Willing (13)
Wallace High School

IMAGINE

Imagine a world taken o'er by robots
Imagine 'em teachin' yae tae.
Imagine what wid happen if yae got a sum wrang
They'd slash yae like ham awe day.
They'd hit yae
They'd whip yae
Like ma granny said they used tae.
But whit a dinnie understand is they said it
wis the gid auld days.
Imagine yae working for robots awe day
Being a slave without pay.
Awe it wid be terrible
But here's a point.
Why don't inventors just no invent them!

Barry Maclean (12)
Wallace High School

CLASH OF THE TITANS (CLYDEBANK V ST MIRREN)

Watching in the stand, down on the match
Hoping that the Bankie's goalie is going to make a good catch,
Especially when Barry Lavetty makes a good strike,
It could be deadly to the score-line tonight.

Big Basher scores to put the Buddies in the lead,
But is short-lived when the Bankies score with the heid.
Oohhh! go the St Mirren crowd when Clydebank score,
But the Bankies stand goes up in a great big roar,
The score stands at one all,
but we hope Clydebank score another goal.

The ref blows the whistle to mark half-time,
The mad rushing fans start to whine,
Because the coffee, tea, Bovril and pies are in short supply.
Have you ever seen grown men cry?

Basher, McWorter, Mendez and all,
Give their best but canny keep control of the ball.
The Bankies with skill and grace,
have St Mirren running all over the place.

Skill, ability he has none, but wee Bunter can still have the odd
mazey run.
This way and that way, he keeps a hold of the ball.
The St Mirren defence have no chance a tall,
With the goal in his sight and the ball on his right, he makes an
absolutely fabulous strike.
The ball in the back of the net and the goalie distraught,
This is the one the goalie should have caught.

The whistle blows at full-time,
Much to the delight of the supporting 29!

Clare Harris (13)
Wallace High School

ME

If everyone in the world is called *me,*
And *me* wanted to fight me.
Who would win?
Me would win.
Who would get the blame.
Me would get the blame,
Then the police would come.
Who would be arrested?
Me would be arrested.
Then *me* was took to the police station.
There *me* was put in a cell.
With all the other *mes.*
Then they started to fight again,
Then they were took to court,
Where they said *'It was me'*
And the judge said *'It was not me'*
And they were all given a *warning.*

James Stewart (13)
Wallace High School

WHAT I THINK OF THE TIGER

The tiger is a very fierce creature,
It has two very special features.
Its first special feature is it's very sharp teeth,
On which its victims come to grief.
The second feature is its stripes,
Which it uses for camouflage all day, all night.

The tiger uses its strong legs for running,
It really is very cunning.
It uses its legs to chase its prey,
But the antelope can see her and runs away.

The tiger has very good sight,
It can see its prey even in the night.
Through the bush it can see the deer,
The tiger can smell the fear.
Then suddenly if leaps out from behind the tree,
The deer just then starts to flee.

John Morton (12)
Wallace High School

EVACUATION

That morning our house was still,
There was a cloud of sadness formed around us.
We walked to the station in silence,
Taking in all the houses and people.
We never knew if we would see them again.
The station was busy with children
All with gas masks and name tags.
Some mothers were hysterical
Kneeling at their children's feet
Making sure they hadn't forgotten anything.
Others weren't anything at all, just staring.
The town clock chimed nine while the train whistle blew,
Signalling their goodbyes.
Unspeaking we trundled into the carriages,
Just staring at our mothers and thinking of home.
The train started to pull out of the station,
Slowly at first.
One look back,
Then we were gone.

Erin McGowan (13)
Wallace High School

Pets In My Family

Pets are important to us all,
They run to our sides when we call.
The pets in this poem are important to me,
These are the pets of my family.

Kimmey was a stray at first,
But into my dad's house he burst.
And into all the families hearts,
He and my dad were never apart.

Then came Brandy, Kimmey's son,
A little bundle full of fun.
He used to sit on grandad's chair,
But only when he wasn't there.

Never was there a finer cat,
Trixie never missed a rat.
She would sit and listen to what Gran had to say,
Until she strangely ran away.

Jasper was the latest pet,
He was tiny when we met.
Soon he grew to twice his size,
And caught five mice in just two tries.

Toby the dog was the newest recruit,
He sat on your hand like a big piece of fruit.
And soon he would bark and chase all the birds,
And learn 'sit' and 'stay' and some other words.

Simba the cat's only one year old,
But already has a girlfriend, or so I've been told.
With his big bushy tail, like an old orange sock
He looks really cool when he walks down the block.

These are the pets which are important to me
These are the pets in my family.

David Sherman (13)
Wallace High School

INTERGALACTIC DAY

We all went on a spaceship
To travel to the moon
To see the theme park and intergalactic zoo.

There were monkey-looking creatures
Elephants without their trunks.
Hedgehogs without their spikes and
Chipmunks that looked like monks.

Then we went to the theme park
It looked like so much fun
There were aliens selling candyfloss
And beef burgers in their buns.

But the best bit about it
Was the spaceship simulator
It took you round the planets
And showed you the equator.

But now it's time to come down to Earth
It's such a pretty sight
Its deep blue sea and coloured lands
Which you can't see in the darkness of the night.

Graeme Baillie (13)
Wallace High School

Travel To A New Planet

I've lived on this planet all my life
Ecstatic with excitement
Today is the day I travel faster than light
To meet some extra-terrestrial life.
Storming about grabbing my clothes
Hearing the spacecraft land
Loads of new people dawdle around on this new planet.
The time's come, a new life waits.
At customs I'm scanned and re-scanned for contraband.
Walking through the airlock seeing a shiny spacecraft.
Climbing in and closing the hatch
The slight rumble as we lift-off.
So excited as I undo my seat belt
Then violently pulled back into my seat
A minute later and nearly there
A violent vibrating starts.
Thinking I'm going to see my lunch again.
Then it's all over and we touch down.
The hatch blasts open and a tall man with a beard says
'Welcome to *Earth*, the planet where the human race was raised.'

David Stuart (13)
Wallace High School

Trees

Do you like trees
Swaying in the breeze?

Trees are like elderly people,
Towering over you,
Just watching, watching
Over you.

Do you like the sound
Of the crisp crunch
Of the leaves on the autumn floor?

Leave are not just green
They are millions of different shades of green.
They are orange, red and even purple in autumn,
But I am still keen
On green.

Emily Hutton (13)
Wallace High School

TRUE BLUE

There is a team I really love,
In the league they are above.
Last year they were almost at ten,
Then we had to start again.

I love it when they score goals,
If it's Jorg Albertz or Michael Moles
When the other team put the ball in the net,
Then I really begin to sweat.

We have a stadium called Ibrox,
Where there is a conference room where players talk.
Now we are in Europe,
So teams better 'beware'.
Looking forward to the final,
We will do anything to be there.

It all began in eighteen seventy-three,
That's why Glasgow Rangers is the team for me.

Gary Miller (13)
Wallace High School

POEM

What is a poem?
Poems are everything
The air that surrounds us,
Or the song a whale sings.

A poem can be anything,
Anything you want it to be.
Imaginative writing,
Mind pictures you can see.

How should a poem be read?
Read it how you want to.
Nice and cheery, slow and calm,
Or even sad and blue.

What can it be about?
It can be about everything.
Trees, wind and sea,
Or even a bird trying to sing.

Where can a poem be read?
Anywhere you want to read it.
In a playground, in the school,
I recommend a dark place, candlelit.

Katrina Button (13)
Wallace High School

THE GATE

The gate is mysterious, gloomy and dark.
Its bars are covered in rust.

The gate is huge, old and forbidding.
Who knows what's behind it?

The gate is lonely broken and stuck.
Its lock is broken shut.

The gate is tired, sad and angry.
Covered in vandalism.

This is the gate.

Andrew Glass (13)
Wallace High School

SCOTLAND

Scotland is my favourite place,
The food has an excellent taste.
Haggis, chips, Iron-bru,
I love it all, I really do.

The history here is really great,
Things are found from every date.
Some of it is really old, so,
Off to a museum it will go.

There is also a lot of wildlife here,
That includes birds, fish and deer.
There are a few people that really do care,
About the animals that are very rare.

The people here can be real mates,
Which I think is really great.
Scotland is the best place ever,
Could I live anywhere else?
Never!

Adele Mullarkey (12)
Wallace High School

MIND THE GAP

Standing waiting for the tube to come,
Looking around many different faces and races.
Dark, light, pale and bright faces,
Everyone speaking different languages,
Dutch, Spanish, French and Italian,
All forms, shapes and sizes,
Fat, thin, tall and small.

Hundreds of items of different clothing.
Smartly dressed business men in suits,
Shirt and tie with gleaming shoes.
Skirts, shorts, tracksuits and trousers.
Casually dressed tourists in tracksuits and worn trainers.
Fashion, old, bright and dull.

Here comes the train heading for Euston,
Everyone waiting to jump aboard.
Mind the gap!
A race to get on and dive for a space,
This train is calling *Euston . . .*
The trains stops at Euston,
Another race to get out.
Mind the gap!

Jill Jackson (13)
Wallace High School

I HAD A DREAM

I had a dream
That humans were mean.
We cut down the trees,
Polluted the air,
Killed animals
And stole their hair.

I woke up with a scream,
My mum ran in
With her fur coat in her hand
Her burning fag filling the air.
She sat by my side on my pine wooden floor
And asked why I screamed.
I replied,
I had a dream.

Jamie Aldridge (13)
Wallace High School

SCHOOL

School is boring
Nag, nag, nag,
Home economics is a drag,
I hate writing,
I hate all the rules,
They're only there to trick me,
To make me feel a fool.

Lunchtime is great,
I love all the food,
Pizza and chips,
Taste really good.

But then the bell goes,
It's back into class.
More things I don't know,
More questions to ask.

I wish there was no such thing as school
So then I would be free to fly by
Like the birds in the sky.

Arron John Russon (12)
Wallace High School   .

POEMS ABOUT POETRY

Poems are to any language
What peacocks are to birds.
Verses page upon page
Not prose or any old words.

In this field there has never been such variety
There is no compulsory propriety
It could be humorous or serious
Nostradamus' prophesies or maybe mysterious.

Narrative or dealing with emotion
There is talent in great proportion.
In French or Latin
Or as smooth as satin
But always in continuos motion.

Liam Dickson (13)
Wallace High School

THE SEA

The endless blue ocean like the endless blue sky,
Filled with lots of different creatures,
Whales, dolphins and sharks,
But in the depths what else lurks
In the shadows in the deep?
What kind of creatures creep?
Big, scary monsters with ten eyes and ten feet,
They just sit there and stare.
But on the surface the sea is beautiful,
The big white waves splashing on the shore,
Roll back into the ocean endlessly,
And then come back once more.

Lorna Stewart (13)
Wallace High School

FOR DAYS IN THE PAST

The old apple tree sat withered and bare,
The crisp autumn leaves were no longer there.
The summer fruits had fallen and gone,
The corner was dark where the sun had once shone.

The old slab path sat cracked and worn,
The canvas seat had long ago torn.
A gentle breeze made the long grass sway,
And dandelion fairies floated swiftly away.

All living creatures were dead or gone,
Nothing lived in that place for long.
All the sweet flowers had bloomed their last,
The long grass mourned for days in the past.

A nuclear factory where the cottage had been,
Instead of home baking; poisons unseen.
No people for miles, no people to care,
The old apple tree, sat withered and bare.

Anna Murphy (13)
Wallace High School

THE MILLENNIUM

The millennium is here
Children are screaming
Parents are wishing each other Happy New Year.
The bells are ringing
Everybody's singing 'The millennium is here.'
Glasses are clashing,
Corks are popping,
As they celebrate the millennium year.

Alison Buchanan (11)
Wallace High School

RANGERS

I have a favourite football team,
Rangers is their name.
I like to go and watch them,
When winning is their aim.

All the players celebrate,
When booting in the goals.
They do cartwheels and somersaults,
Around striker Michael Mols.

The 'Gers are now in Europe,
So foreign teams beware!
You will have to come to Ibrox,
And then you'll get a scare.

Billy Honeyman (13)
Wallace High School

MY HOUSE

My house is a fast flowing river,
With people flooding in and out.
My house is a taxi company,
With people ringing for lifts.
My house is a refugee camp,
With friends and family camping over.
My house is a mayor's house,
With orders being made to everyone.
My house is a fun house,
Where people are happy.

Robert Eadie (13)
Wallace High School

RONALDO

Ronaldo is a skillful man,
Football is his game.
I'm his biggest fan,
And he has shot to fame.

He can do some tricks,
And head the ball too.
His head is like a brick,
When he heads the ball to you.

He says 10
I don't understand.
He's come all the way from Brazil,
To play in a foreign land.

He is a great player,
He really is the best.
So wait for the World Cup,
And we'll put him to the test!

Robert McLachlan (11)
Wallace High School

IN SPACE

Space is a place where astronauts go
To find out what's out there so they know.
They float about and don't touch the ground,
They wear big boots so they can get down.
They eat bagged food that's very dry
And it doesn't taste so good, I wonder why?

Stacy Tully (12)
Wallace High School

THE TENTH PLANET

I want to be a famous man,
I've found a way to do it.
I am a solar system fan,
I'll find the tenth planet if I can.

I'll need a strong telescope,
So I can see the tenth planet.
I wonder if I'll find it,
I can only hope for I need a strong telescope.

I went away and bought one,
The strongest one out yet.
I need some people to help me,
I need all the help I can get.

I have got all the help,
And I've started to look.
I haven't found it, that's not fair,
There must be a tenth planet somewhere.

I think I have found it,
Yes, yes I have!
I see it, it's a greeny-blue colour,
I'm going to be famous man,
Yes!

Adam Brown (11)
Wallace High School

SPACE POEM

Planets are round,
They float in the night.
I stand on the ground
And look at the
Beautiful sight.

Stars twinkle in the dark sky
Like shining fire flies.
The moon is like a
light bulb shining bright,
Showing the way in the dark night.

Nikki White (13)
Wallace High School

MY PETS

I have a dog called Honey,
I love her more than millions of money.
She's cute, she's wee and she's mad like me,
That's my wee dog Honey.

I have a budgie called Snowy
Who flies about in her cage.
She eats, she tweets and she sings and swings,
That's my wee budgie Snowy.

I have a fish called Melba,
I called her that because she's peach.
She eats fishy flakes and floating sticks,
That's my wee fish Melba.

My gran has a cat called Molly.
I kind of say she's mine.
She's black, she's white and she likes to fight
With my gran, grandad and me!

I have a dog called Honey, a budgie called Snowy,
A fish called Melba and a cat called Molly.
And I love them all the same,
'Cause they're all very tame.

Alana O'Hare (12)
Wallace High School

THE ONCE LOYAL FRIEND

In primary until secondary
A once loyal friend
Stood by my side
Whatever.
A friend she was
But now is gone
Moved as fast as a chess pawn.
In one small second she changed
Forever.
As you go through thick and thin
Remember this.
Like some string
Once apart,
Never the same again.

Lana Kerr (13)
Wallace High School

MILLENNIUM

3 . . . 2 . . . 1 . . . Happy New Year!
The millennium 2000 is now here.
People dance, children scream,
And there's the nicest fireworks I've ever seen.
Music blaring up and down the street
And lots of lovely things to eat.
Everyone cheering and wishing good luck
And all your family kissing . . . *yuck!*
People drinking wine and beer,
Because we're all celebrating this millennium year.

Nyree Bell (12)
Wallace High School

FUTURE VOICES EVERYWHERE

Dark at night
No one can see
Crowded everywhere
No one can see
I wonder
What the future
Will be like
Exciting things
To do
Riding bikes
And visiting
The
Zoo
Every year
A bright
Star will
Appear in the sky
People in their sixties
Learning to ski-jump
Deep in the future
Mercury has just passed
Mars
The stars are
Blooming like
The moon
I think that's
What it's going to
Be like
In the year
2083.

Sarah-Jane Reid (13)
Wallace High School

WHERE IS THE FLAG?

In the European parliament,
Lots of flags stand tall.
The Union Jack, the French and German flags,
To name a few.
But not the flag of the European Union,
No stars stand on their navy-blue backing,
No stars in the sky.
It's everywhere else,
Doors, walls, windows, and even the press shop is star-shaped.
No flag, a government, governors, we do have a flag.
But not shown,
Hidden,
Somewhere.

In the European Parliament,
Where is the flag,
Mr Patten?
Where have you hidden it?
Are you using it as a tablecloth?
Then what have you done with the pole?
Is it holding up your desk?
Or have the workmen pinched it?
The cord, is it keeping your shoes on?
Where are the stars from the sky?
No flag; a government, governors, we *do* have a flag.
But not shown,
Hidden,
Somewhere.

In the European parliament,
Where is the flag
Ms Albright?
Where have you hidden it?
Has your office gained a new carpet?
Have you made a dress from it?
The pole, have you turned it into a pogo stick?
Maybe that's where it's gone!
Is that a new belt?
Have you borrowed the cord?
Where are the stars from the sky?
No flag; a government, governors, we *do* have a flag.
But not shown,
Hidden,
Somewhere.

I wonder,
Where is the flag?

Karen Holden (13)
Wallace High School

THE CLOCK IN THE ROOM

My grandad is deaf but he can still hear the clicks,
The old clock in the hall goes click, click, click.
My grandad pretended it was a trick,
At twelve o'clock at midnight
The bell goes
And it starts clicking,
Again the clicks always click,
But one day my grandad was sick,
He went to bed,
Next morning he died
And the clock didn't click.

Colin Cairney (12)
Wallace High School

UNDER THE BED

'Mum, mum there's something under my bed!'
'It's OK, it's OK' she reassuringly said.
'But there is, but there is and it won't go away,
It says nasty things like, I'm going to stay.
It looks so ugly and slimy and fat,
It really is a very big *brat!*
Have you not got anything that will kill him dead?
Like Dad's socks, last weeks dinner or rotten old bread.'
'But son, oh! son that will not work,
It likes dirty things like rubbish and dirt.
But don't you worry he won't be here long
Tonight will be full of drunken song
For tonight you see is the last of '99
And everyone will be drinking lots of beer and wine,
Scary monsters can't stand the smell of alcohol
And he'll hate it so much he'll run right through your wall.
Then you'll never see it again, not even a peep
And after that you'll finally get some sleep.'

Roy Shirlaw (12)
Wallace High School

PLANET POEM

Why is the sun yellow?
Why is Mars red?
Are there Martians, or are they all dead?

Out of the planets,
Out of the stars,
I think I would rather go to Mars.

Will I go to Venus?
Will I go to Mars?
I might just go and visit the stars.

I went to Venus which shines like a star,
Through a telescope it doesn't look so far.
The clouds are green and made of acid rain,
I don't think I want to go back there again.

Claire Stennett (13)
Wallace High School

WAITING FOR WAR

When I am older
I will join the army.
I will wear a uniform
And travel in trucks.

When I am in my barracks
I will be cleaning my shoes.
I will be standing by for war,
Ready to see blood and gore.

But when I am in the army
There might not be a war.
I might not use my gun,
Then I won't see blood and gore.

When I am in the army
I hope there is no war.
I hope I don't use my gun,
I'll stay in my barracks waiting for war
But I hope it never comes.

Callum Scoular (13)
Wallace High School

TRUCKING

In the future I will drive a truck
I'll only need maps if I really get stuck.
I'll stop at towns and far away places,
Dropping off goods and seeing new faces.

Pick up new cargo and on down the track,
Passing other travellers and always looking back.
Stop at the station to eat and rest,
Back on the road and full of zest.

Five more hours till I get home,
My last stop is the Millennium Dome.
My day is done and homeward bound,
Soon in my bed sleeping safe and sound.

Robin Boyle (12)
Wallace High School

MY CAT SHEBA

Meowing, meowing
all the time,
You never get peace
until you give her food.
Easy come,
Easy go,
In the morning you will never be late,
She will wake you up early
by licking your face
with her rough tongue.
She's got razor teeth
and sharp claws,
But at the end of the day sleeps like an angel.

Joanna McLean (13)
Wallace High School

PLANET POEMS

The black night shines away up high,
Planets twinkle in the sky,
Comets can make people die.
There is a black hole up above,
But the moon is white just like a dove.
I would like to see what is up there,
At the stars I always stare.

Planets are so vast, so big,
They move around and around playing tig.
The planet Mars is so red,
At night when I go to bed.
There are constellations in the sky,
The hunter is a big, big guy.
And when they all go away,
It's time to start another day.

Mark McPhee (12)
Wallace High School

PLANET POEM

Far away from the Earth
What planets will I see next,
Will it be Mars, Neptune or Pluto?
I see bright stars shine in the sky,
Asteroids whiz by
Like birds that fly.
The colours red, yellow, green and blue,
The sound of the crash as we land shakes the crew.
Silence as we come out the spaceship,
The only noise is the sound of us breathing.

Stephanie Smith (13)
Wallace High School

IN THE FUTURE

The future will be a nice place,
Every year there will be a mouse race,
Every person will have an alien face
And a white mouse will always win the mouse race.

The future will be much, much bigger,
The gunmen will never pull a trigger,
A new animal in France will be tasted
And Wallace High School will be wasted.

In the cities and in the towns there will be more shops,
The most gorgeous beer will be lager Topps,
The football will be very numb
And everybody will still love their mum.

When we go down to Wembley,
The English will attack the Scots,
We don't really care,
'Cause we'll take the English lot.

There will be no more schools in the future,
Hip, hip hooray,
There will be no more schools in the future,
So we can all go out and play.

John Buchanan (12)
Wallace High School

SPACE

Flying through space
At an awful place.

I see a bit of Mars,
Also all the stars.

The stars are bright,
They come out at night.

The asteroid belt
Came down with a pelt.

Lorraine Rankin (13)
Wallace High School

THE FUTURE

The future will be
like a whole new world.
People enjoying each
other's company.

With new computers
that kids can sit at and
the teacher talks to them,
So kids don't need to go
to school.

Buses can run every two
minutes.
And shops can come to you.

With aliens dancing
round the stars.
Jupiter at your doorstep.
Mercury in your room.
Come on board and we
will have some fun.

The future will be great,
That's what I think anyway.
Come on 1999 hurry up and go,
Hooray for the millennium.

Wendy Russell (12)
Wallace High School

POLICE

Now I'm grown-up and fulfilled my dream,
I'm in the police force like one of the team.
We all wear uniforms and funny hats,
Our jobs are more than rescuing cats.

At times it's rough and makes me sad,
Catching criminals that are really bad.
All of them are going to jail
With no one there to pay their bail.

It's not all bad - it can be fun,
Especially when I use my stungun.
My wife and kids are safe and sound,
They're proud I'm a policeman all year round.

James Thomson (13)
Wallace High School

PLANET POEM

I'm sitting here,
I'm sitting there,
There's nothing else to do but stare.
I look around and stare and stare,
But still I see nothing there.
But suddenly I look up and see
A comet slowly passing me.
The Earth is round,
The moon is bright
And the stars shine just like the moonlight.

Vicki Campbell (13)
Wallace High School

SPACE

Will this machine really work in an exploration up to space,
If it could I would be beyond the human race.
If I could go to Neptune I would see the two moons in a race.

Asteroids go flying through outer space,
Going through all the galaxies as if they were of no
importance to the human race.
If I could just ride one, that would just be the best.

Stars, stars they are so bright
Like fire-flies flying all through the night.
But you can't go up because they are too bright
And you might end up just getting a fright.

The moon is so white,
It is like a boomerang coming back at night,
But meanwhile it goes whizzing round the Earth
Just as fast as light.

Kenneth Anderson (13)
Wallace High School

ANIMALS

There are a lot of animals
And some of them are scary.
There are a lot of baldy ones
But most of them are hairy.
Some of them climb trees,
Some live on the ground.
Look at them all
And listen to their sounds.

If you're going to the jungle,
Never go by yourself.
If you're going to the jungle,
Go with someone else.
There are a lot of animals
You wouldn't want to meet
And remember to protect yourself,
Wear something on your feet!

Gary Drummond (12)
Wallace High School

MILLENNIUM

The millennium is coming
And everything is happening.
Everyone is excited,
People rushing from shop to shop.
Ya know the phrase,
'Shop till you drop'.
Well there are
Only so many days to go,
People say oh no.
People will be having parties
To celebrate the millennium.
When the bells chime
At midnight
It will be the end of nineteen ninety-nine.
All you hear is cheers,
Some may shed a tear,
So get off your chair
And throw your hands in the air
Because the millennium is here.

Claire Griffiths (13)
Wallace High School

FIREWORKS

Yellow, red, blue, orange and green,
Oh look at those colours, what a scene.
Bright colours falling around,
A lot of people not making a sound.

Circles, spirals, stars and lines,
Shapes so great with colours which shine.
They're shooting up, up to the sky,
They're so very, very high.

Crackle, bang, crackle, bang,
They're going up as if in a gang.
Whiz, pop, whiz, pop,
Please don't go. Never stop.

This is great, to watch the rockets,
Never keep them in your pockets.
Laughter, fun and giggles too,
There's not many left, there's only a few.

Rockets, rain, sparklers and stars,
Fireworks flying over the cars.
Lots and lots of different ones,
Boxes they've carted in must weigh tons.

The bonfire with Guy Fawkes on top,
I don't think it will ever stop.
Guy Fawkes's clothes are burning slow,
Everyone will have to go.

Louise Rawding (13)
Wallace High School

A PICTISH POEM

They left us with some history,
Of that we can be sure,
Carvings ornate, jewellery so great.

These people were tribal and fought
                              for their rights.
They stood through every battle.
They gathered up slaves, a result of these fights.

Charioteers had the status of barons
and made use of these slaves who
worked in their homes and also the land.

Freeholders or farmers worked the land too,
while some worked as blacksmiths
and made weapons so true.

Some people called bards told stories
of their history.
While those called druids maintained
their religion.

Seen as barbarians with long flowing
hair and paint on their bodies.

Louise Gamble (12)
Wallace High School

ORANGE WORLD

The world is like an orange.
The world is big and round.
The peel is like the land all torn.
The inside is like the sea, bumpy like the waves.
The juice is coming out and banging against the rocks.

Craig Flaws (13)
Wallace High School

FREE NATURE

Gently will the river flow,
Lightly will the wind blow,
Sweetly will the birds sing
As the young lambs spring.

As free as it'll fly,
Looking down from the sky,
Watching out for its prey,
The bird will catch if it may.

Past the heather,
Through the trees,
Let him run if he please,
The king of deer.

The river will flow,
The bird will fly,
The stag will run,
The wind will blow.

Amy Maclean (12)
Wallace High School

MY SISTER

I have a little sister,
She is a little pain
And always get what she wants,
It's just not fair, I hate it.

We fight like cat and dog,
We have to share the same room,
It's really not fair,
She always get what she wants.

Jacqueline Stewart (13)
Wallace High School

DRAWING

I enjoy drawing
I do it every night,
I think I'm a good drawer
And rely on my sight.

I buy lots of pencils
From HB to H4,
And if I'm still interested
I'll draw for ever more.
I enjoy drawing
Everything I can,
From the smallest ant
To the biggest man.

Sometimes when I'm bored
I get a pencil and pad,
Then I'm not bored anymore
And then I don't feel bad.

Andrew Millar (12)
Wallace High School

PLANE LIGHTS

Plane lights are so bright.
In the middle of the night.
We can see your lights in the sky.
Your lights are as bright
as a star in the sky at night.
Oh plane, your lights are so bright,
they even catch the corner of your eye every night.

Scott George McKinlay (13)
Wallace High School

MY DOG

My dog is so lazy
but sometimes she is crazy.
Sometimes she is mad
but she is also bad.

My dog's fur is golden brown,
it is even as shiny as a crown.
Her fur is very, very short,
her fur just grows by the quart.

When she was four she got her nose hurt,
she was pricked by a hedgehog,
my poor little dog.
I forgot to say her name, it is Cassie
but after all she is a mad wee lassie.

Craig Ross (12)
Wallace High School

PARENTS' SAYINGS

Don't do that
Do your homework
Go to bed *now*
Tidy your room
No and that's *final*
Feed the animals now
No you can't
Less talking, *more* eating
Practice your music
What did you do at school today?
Well done
Thank you for doing that.

Adonis Vegglis (12)
Wallace High School   .

PARENTS' SAYINGS

Don't you dare do that.
No I don't want you to take my bike.
Don't mutter under your breath.
Go to your room.
You'll do your homework before you go out to play.
Come back at eight o'clock and no later.
Why are you so late?
Put your other trousers on.
Hurry up we'll be late.
Dry the dishes.
Make your bed.
Tidy your own room.
Cut your nails.
No you can't go out to play with her.
Did I say you could have that?
Give me a rest.
What did your last slave die of?
Eat your tea at the table.
How was school today?
That was excellent,
Well done!

Gillian Park (12)
Wallace High School